The Publishers would like to thank the following for permission to reproduce copyright material.

Photo credits

Photos from iStock: p12 Buckingham Palace © Keattikorn; p22 Pharos lighthouse © BORTEL Pavel – Pavelmidi; p38 ice cyrstals © Rumo Photos from Shutterstock: p13 Windsor Castle © sloukam; p24 Longstone lighthouse © Attila JANDI; p39 salt crystals © Ranglen; p40 diamond ring © Serggod; p49 Marianne North © rook76; p50 palki © Jorg Hackemann

Text extracts

pp130–131 'Theseus and the Minotaur' featured on http://myths.e2bn. org; pp136–137 'Do you Believe in Ghosts?' By Rick Barry, Reprinted with permission of Answers in Genesis (www.answersingenesis.org); 'Things that go BUMP in the night!' Adapted from 'Ghosts of the past: 5 haunted royal residences' by Wesley McDermott; pp143–144 'The lion and Albert' by Marriott Edgar, Reprinted with permission of Warner/Chappell Production Music; pp150–151 Adapted from *Lighthouses of England: The North East* by Nicholas Leach and Tony Denton (Foxglove Media, 2010); pp152–153 'Frequently Asked Questions' http://www.rondaarmitage.co.uk/frequently-asked-question © Ronda Armitage; pp158–159 Adapted from *The Hollow Land* by Jane Gardam © David Higham Associates; pp164–165 'The Lady of Shalott' by Alfred Lord Tennyson; pp169–171 468 words adapted from *Crystal & Gem* by R.F. Symes (Dorling Kindersley, 2000). Copyright© Dorling Kindersley Ltd London; pp176–177 Excerpt from 'Macavity: The Mystery Cat' from *Old Possum's Book of Cats* by T.S. Eliot. Copyright 1939 by T.S. Eliot. Copyright © Renewed 1967 by Esme Valerie Eliot. Reprinted with permission of Faber and Faber and Houghton Mifflin Harcourt Publishing Company. All rights reserved; pp181–183 Adapted from *Abundant Beauty* by Marianne North reprinted with permission from Greystone Books Ltd.

Every effort has been made to trace all copyright holders, but if any have been inadvertently overlooked, the Publishers will be pleased to make the necessary arrangements at the first opportunity.

Although every effort has been made to ensure that website addresses are correct at time of going to press, Rising Stars cannot be held responsible for the content of any website mentioned in this book. It is sometimes possible to find a relocated web page by typing in the address of the home page for a website in the URL window of your browser.

Hachette UK's policy is to use papers that are natural, renewable and recyclable products and made from wood grown in sustainable forests. The logging and manufacturing processes are expected to conform to the environmental regulations of the country of origin.

Orders: please contact Bookpoint Ltd, 130 Park Drive, Milton Park, Abingdon, Oxon OX14 4SE. Telephone: (44) 01235 400555. Email: primary@bookpoint.co.uk

Lines are open from 9 a.m. to 5 p.m., Monday to Saturday, with a 24-hour message answering service. Visit our website at www.risingstars-uk.com for details of the full range of Rising Stars publications.

Online support and queries email: onlinesupport@risingstars-uk.com

ISBN: 978 1 51046 936 5

This edition published in 2019 by Rising Stars UK Ltd.

First published in 2015 by Rising Stars UK Ltd.

Rising Stars UK Ltd part of Hodder Education Group

An Hachette UK Company

Carmelite House

50 Victoria Embankment

London EC4Y 0DZ

www.risingstars-uk.com

Impression number 10 9 8 7 6 5 4 3 2 1
Year 2023 2022 2021 2020 2019

Authors: Steph King, Trevor Dixon , Sarah Anne Fernandes, Marie Lallaway, Madeleine Barnes, Laura Collinson and Shareen Mayers

Series Editors: Sarah-Anne Fernandes, Madeleine Barnes and Helen Lewis

Accessibility Reviewer: Vivien Kilburn

Educational Adviser: Josh Lury

Cover design: Burville-Riley Partnership

Illustrations by Ann Paganuzzi and Dave Burroughs

Typeset in India

Printed in India

A catalogue record for this title is available from the British Library.

Contents

ACHIEVE

Mathematics

SATs Practice Papers

Steph King, Trevor Dixon
& Sarah-Anne Fernandes

RISING STARS

Introduction

About the Practice Papers for Mathematics

The tests are written to cover the content domain of the *Key Stage 2 Mathematics test framework for the National Curriculum tests from 2016* (Standards & Testing Agency, 2015).

There are six tests in total, two assessing arithmetic (as per Paper 1 of the National Tests) and four assessing mathematical fluency, solving problems and reasoning (as per Papers 2 and 3 of the National Tests). The practice papers are intended for use during the spring and summer terms of Year 6 in preparation for the National Tests. Each Paper 1 (arithmetic) is worth 40 marks and each Paper 2 or Paper 3 (reasoning) is worth 35 marks. Test demand increases within each test, as in the National Tests, so initial questions are easier than those towards the end of each test.

How to use the Practice Papers

Preparation and timings

1. Help your child prepare for each paper by simulating test conditions.
2. Ensure your child is seated appropriately in front of the paper they are going to work on.
3. Your child will need pens or pencils, rulers and erasers. Angle measurers or protractors, and mirrors, should be available for the *Reasoning tests*. Encourage children to cross out answers rather than rub them out. **Calculators must not be used in the tests**. Tracing paper is no longer allowed to be used in the KS2 National Tests.
4. There are no time limits for the tests but you should be guided by the timings of the actual tests in relation to the number of marks available. Help with reading may be given using the same rules as when providing a reader with the Key Stage 2 tests.

Supporting children during the tests

Before the tests, explain to your child that each test is an opportunity to show what they know, understand and can do. They should try to answer all the questions but should not worry if there are some they can't do.

Many children will be able to work independently in the tests, with minimal support. However, children should be encouraged to 'have a go' at a question, or to move on to a new question if they appear to be stuck.

Marking the tests

Use the mark scheme and your own judgement to award marks. Do not award half marks. Note that a number of questions in each test may require children to do more than one thing for one mark. The mark scheme provides clear guidance in the allocation of marks to support consistent marking of the tests.

It is useful for your child to mark their own test questions from time to time. Your child can look at the test sheets and mark them as you read out the question and answer. You will need to check that your child is marking accurately. This approach also provides an opportunity to recap on any questions that your child found difficult to answer and will help to identify areas of strength or weakness. This can then help support revision planning.

Keep track of your child's score using the table on the inside back cover of this book.

Name:	Class:	Date:	Total marks: /40

Test 1, Paper 1: Arithmetic

1 895 + 200 =

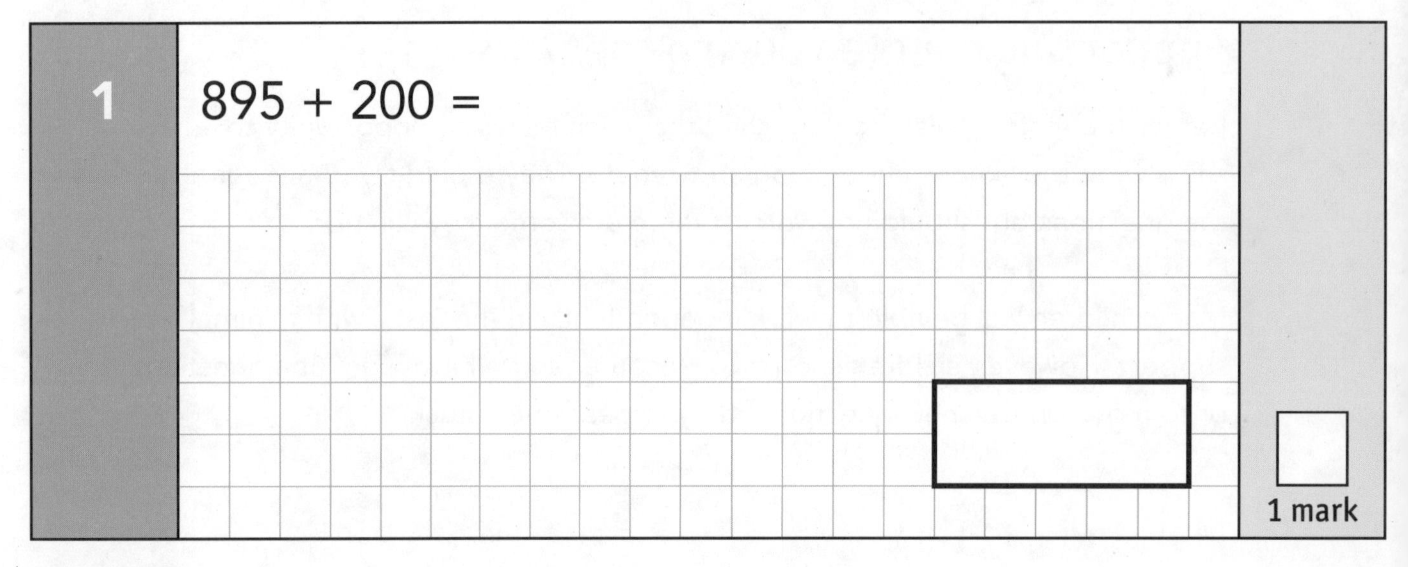

1 mark

2 120 × 5 =

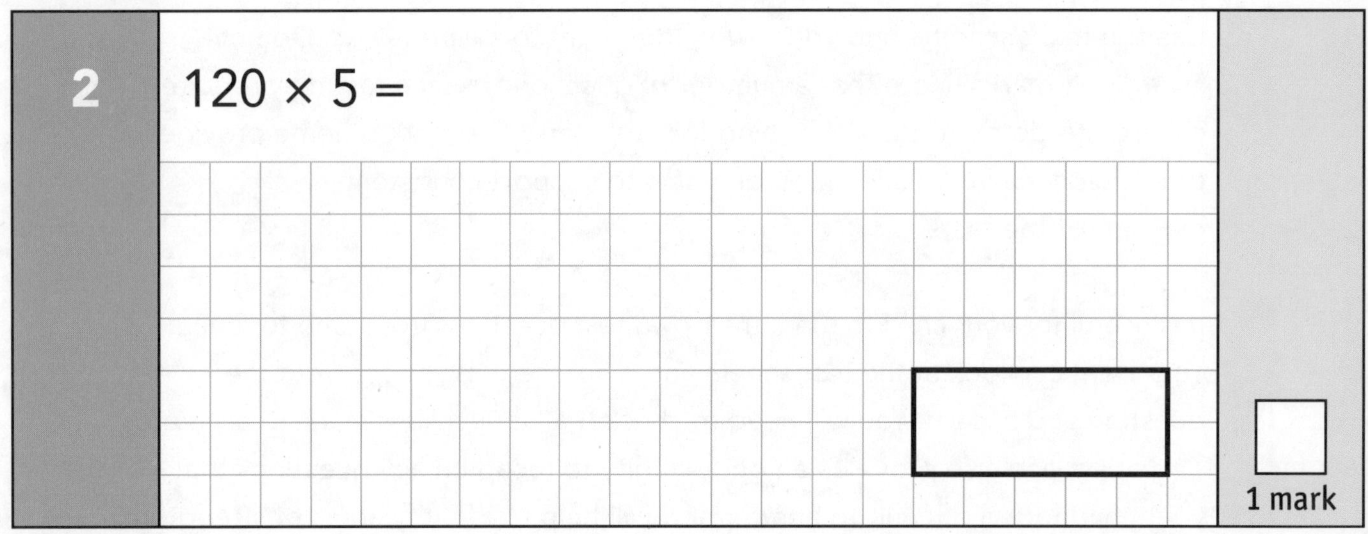

1 mark

3 98 + 412 =

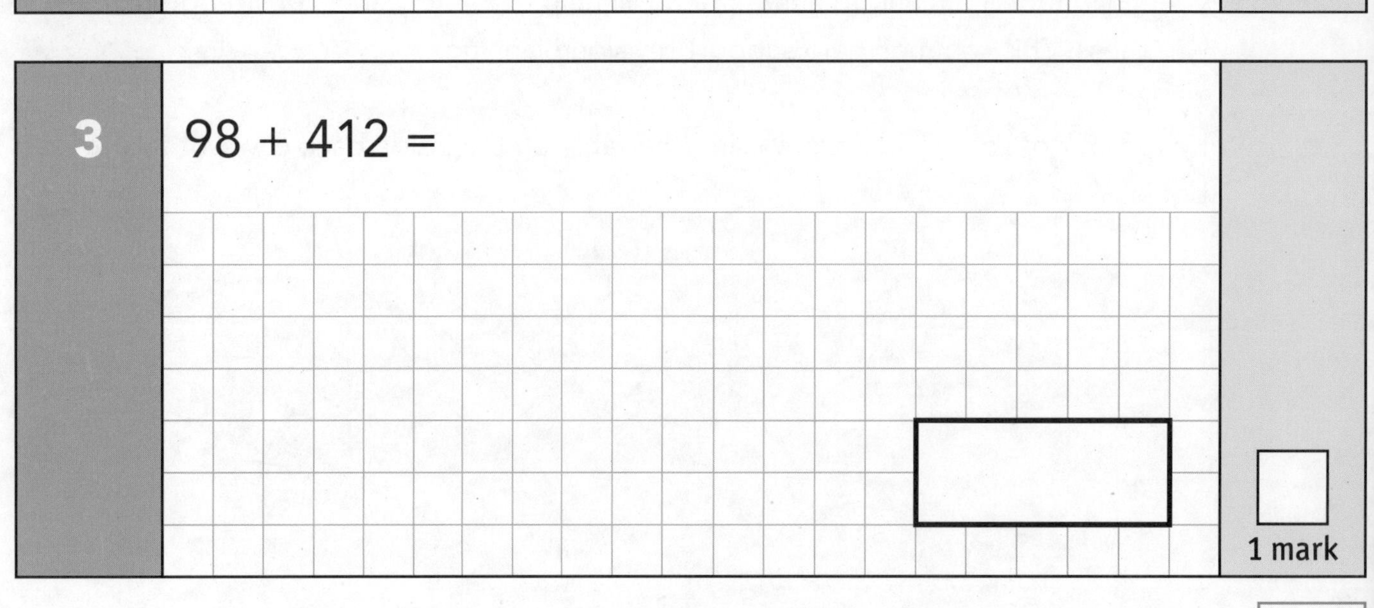

1 mark

/3

Total for this page

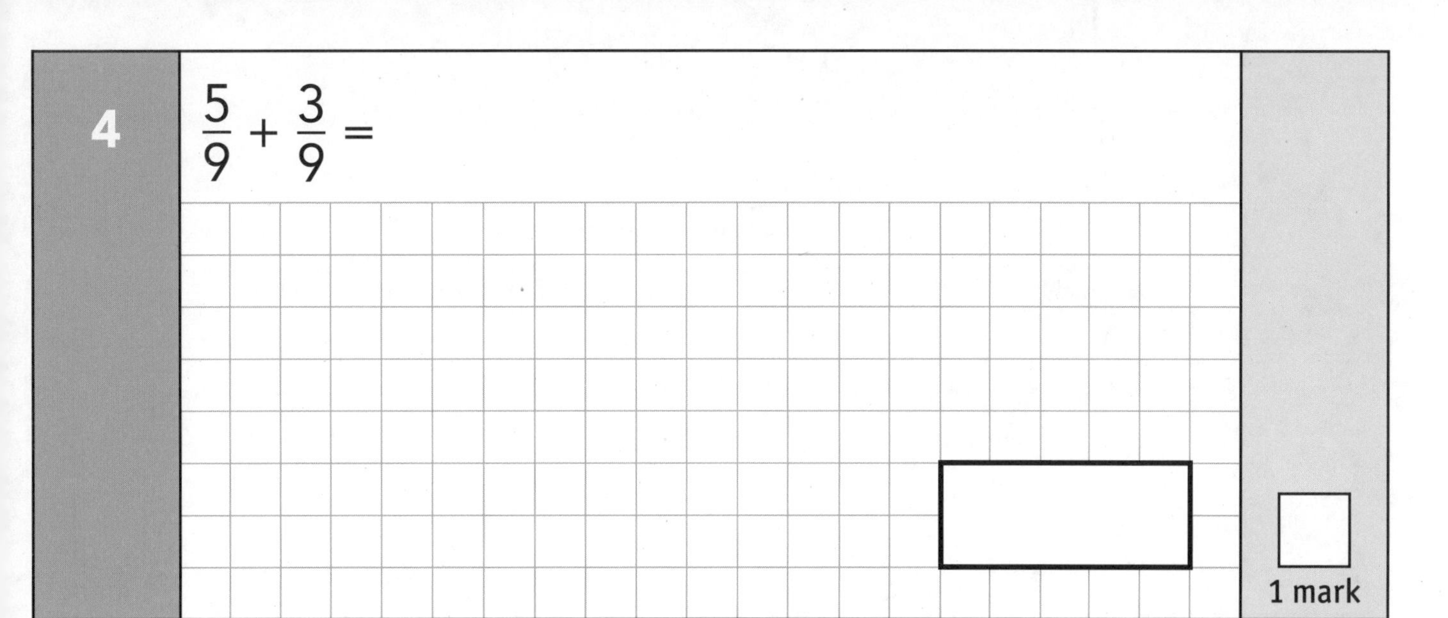

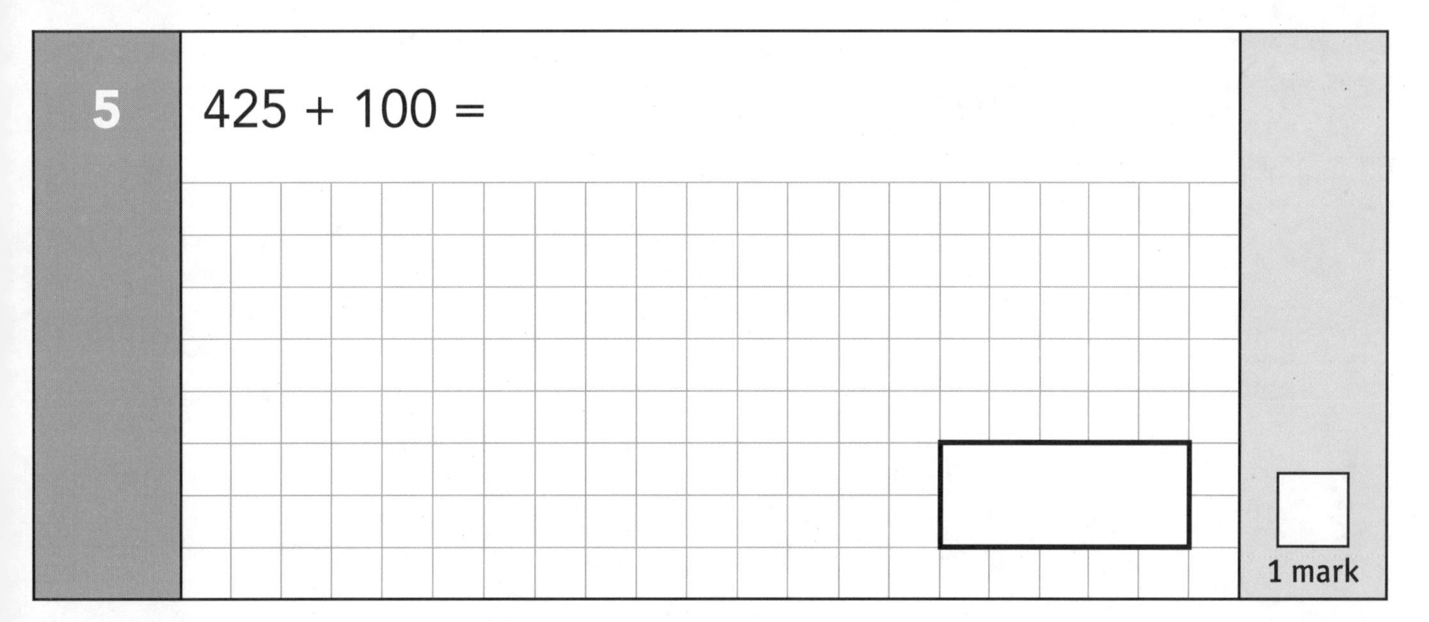

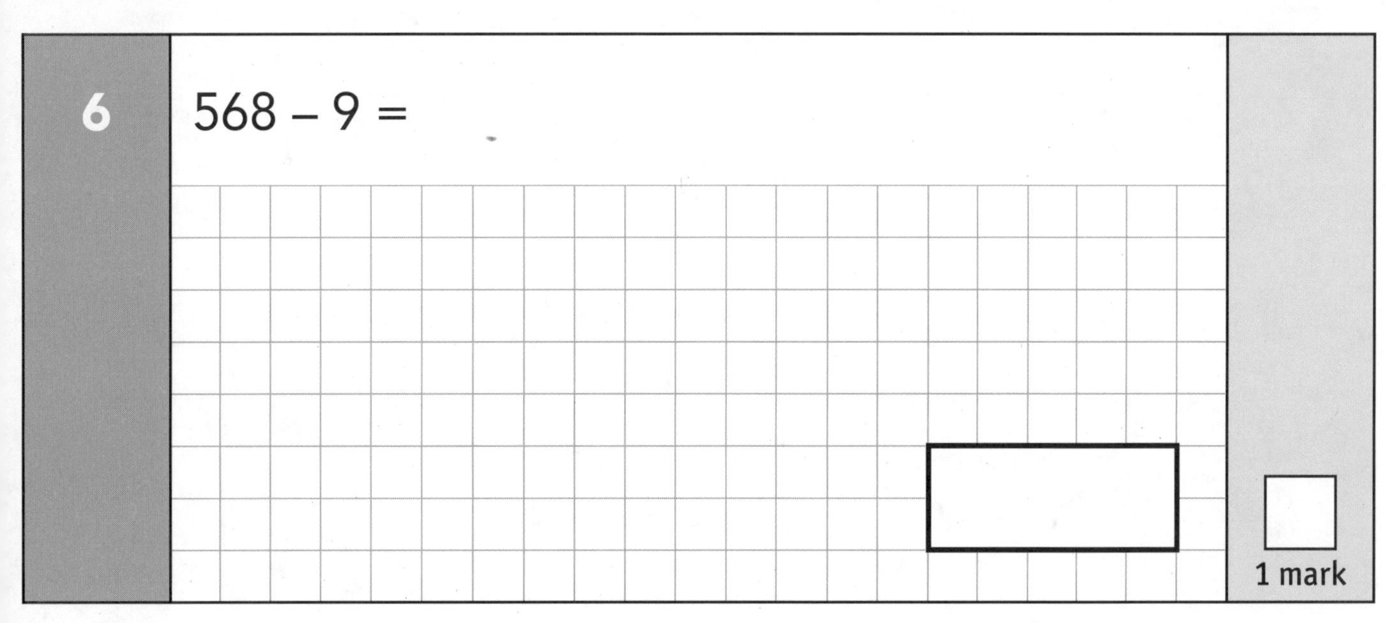

/3

Total for this page

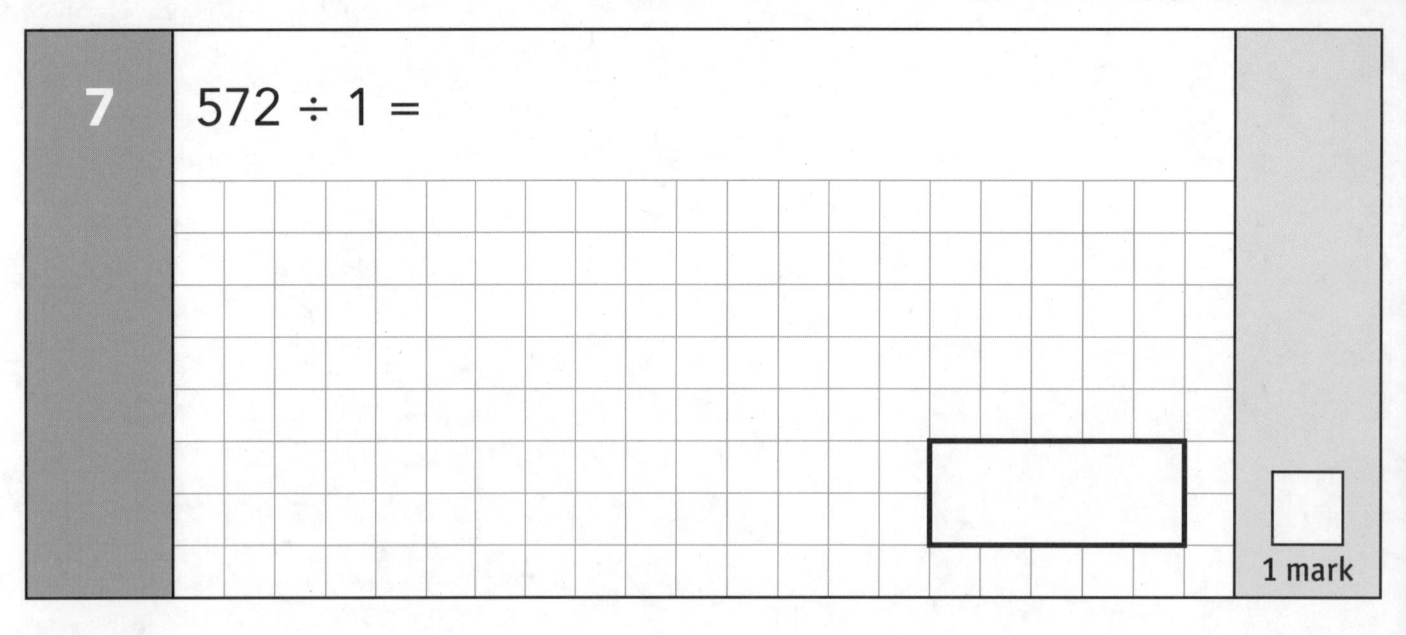

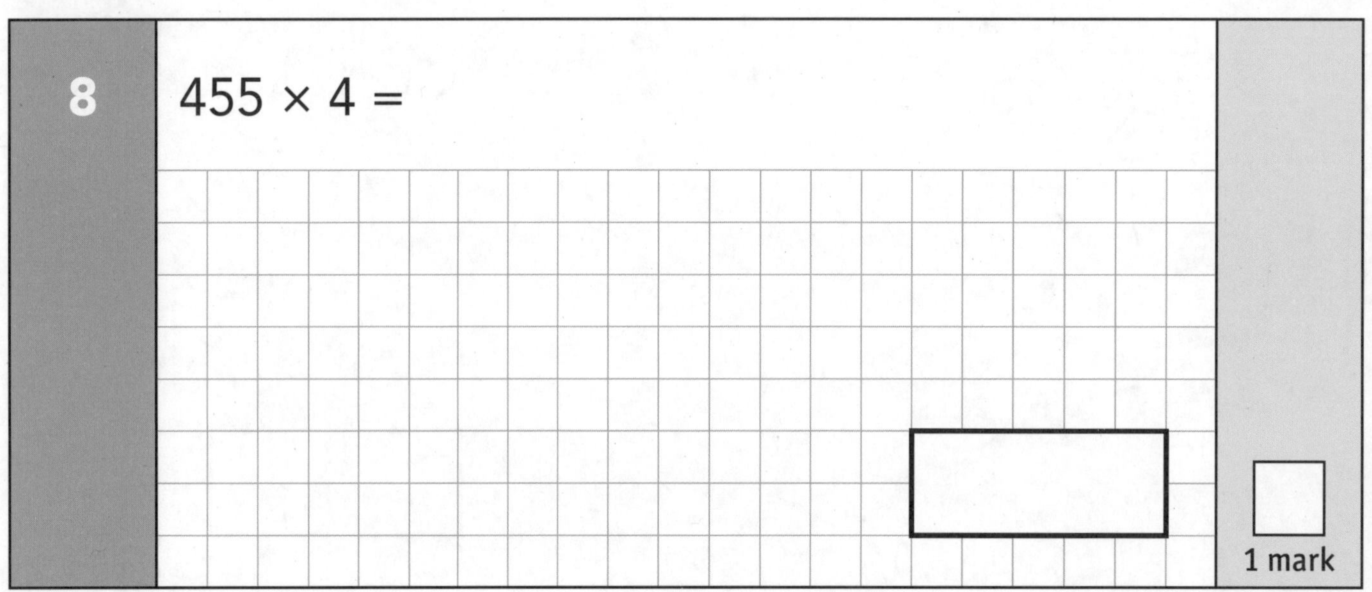

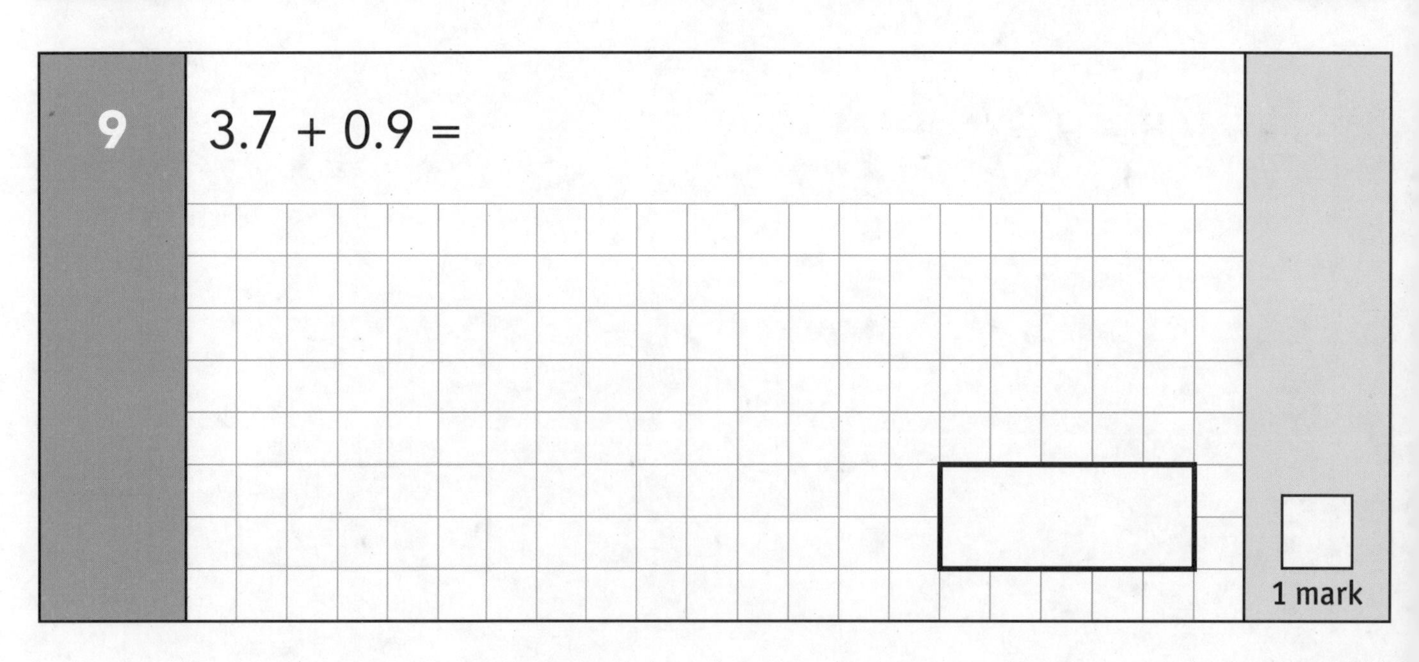

/3

Total for this page

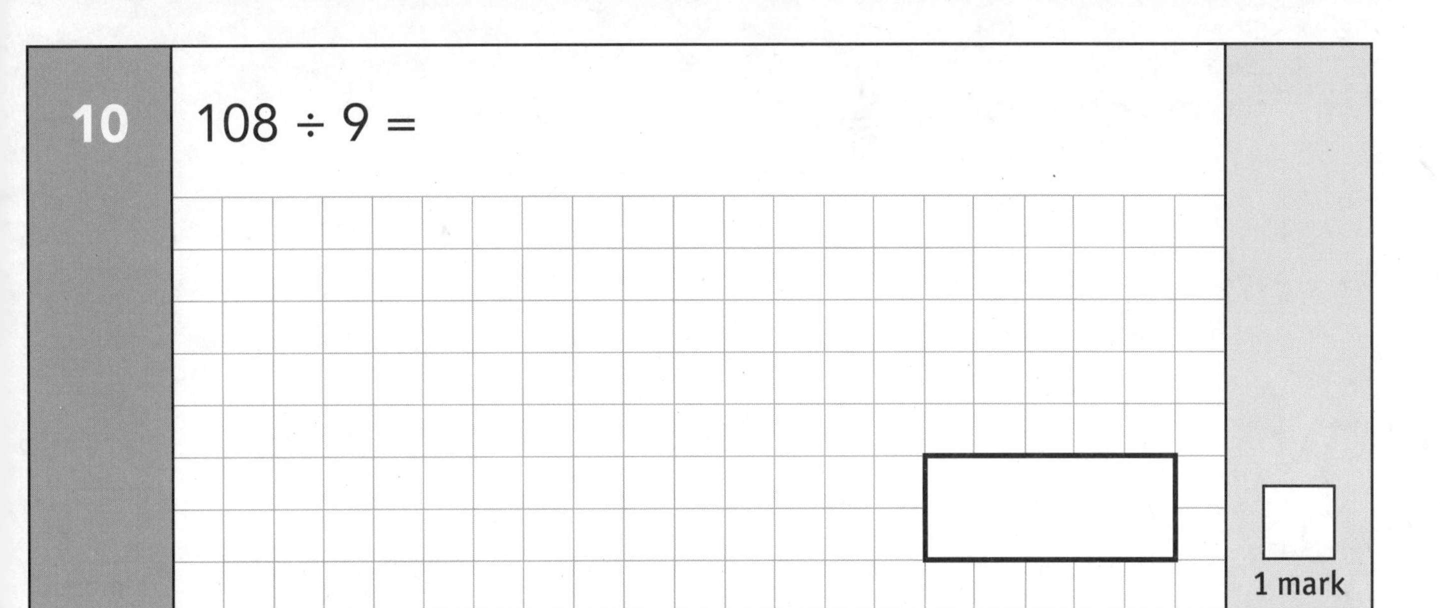

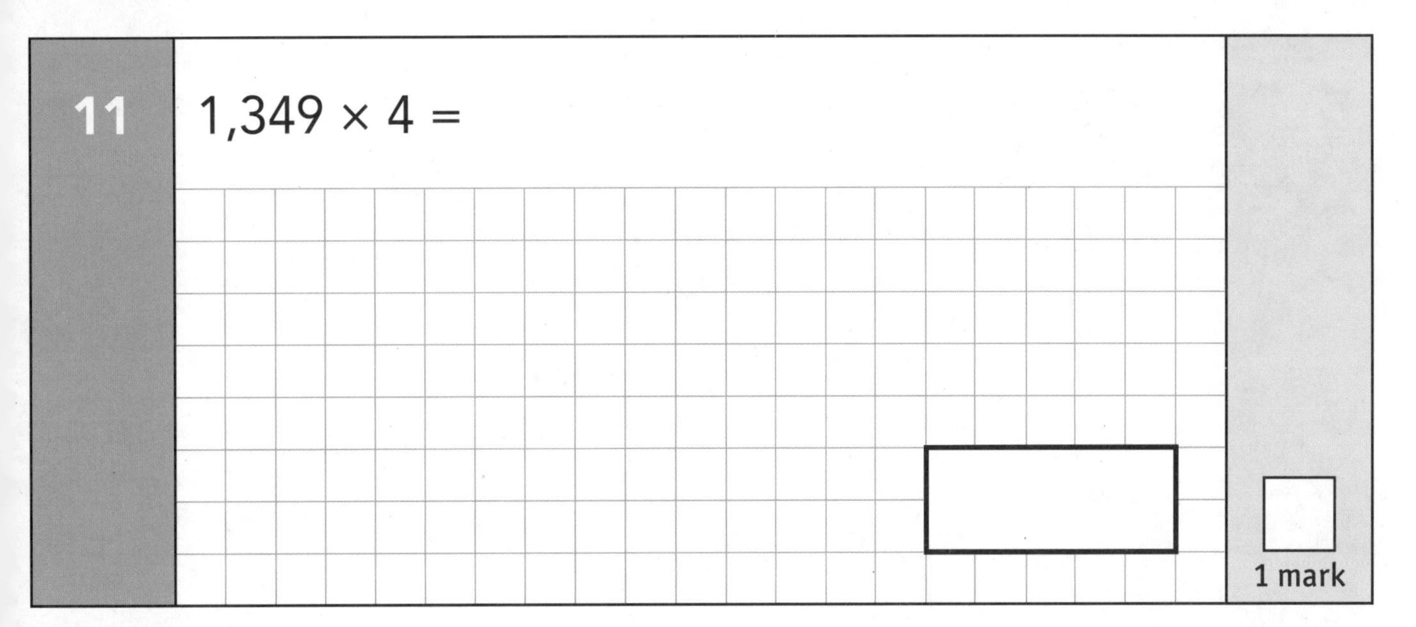

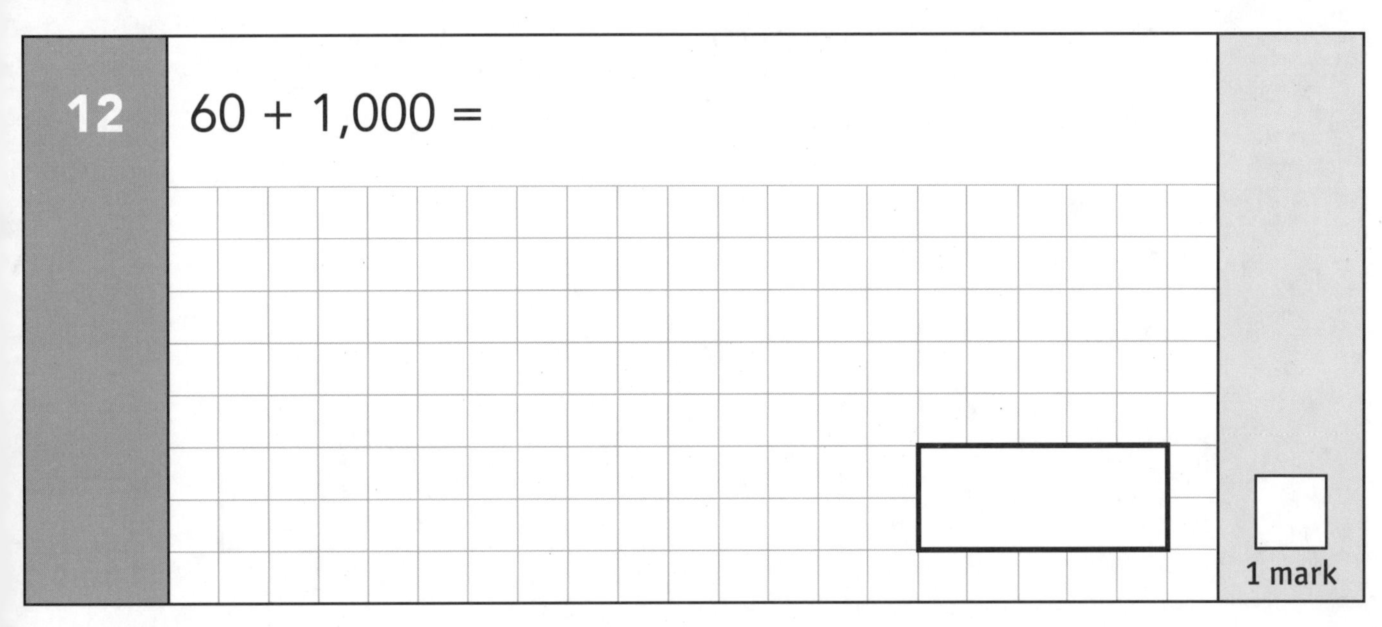

/3

Total for this page

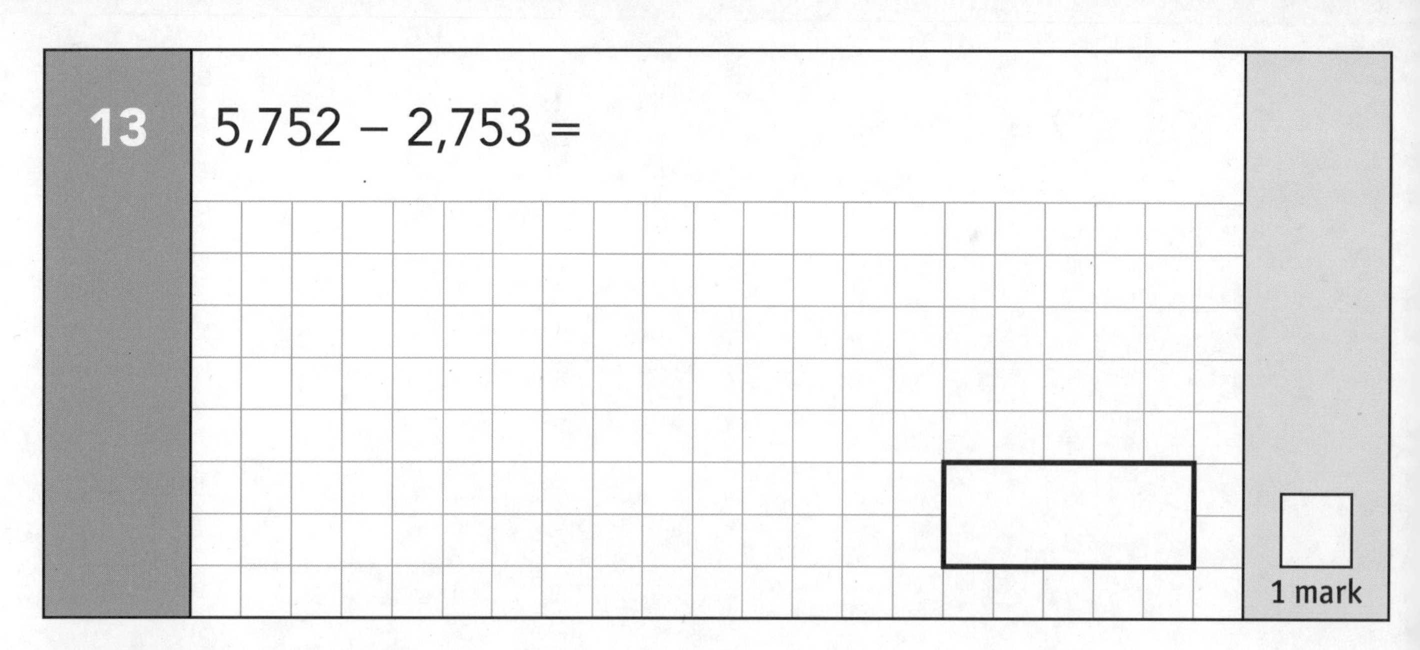

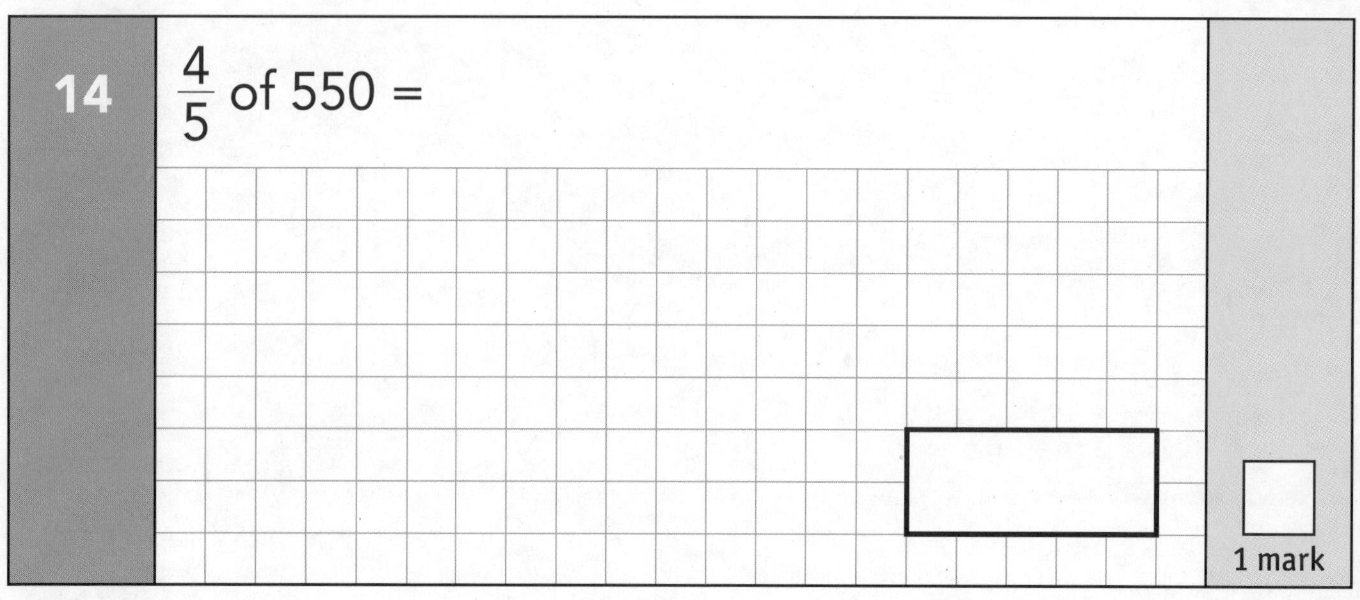

/3

Total for this page

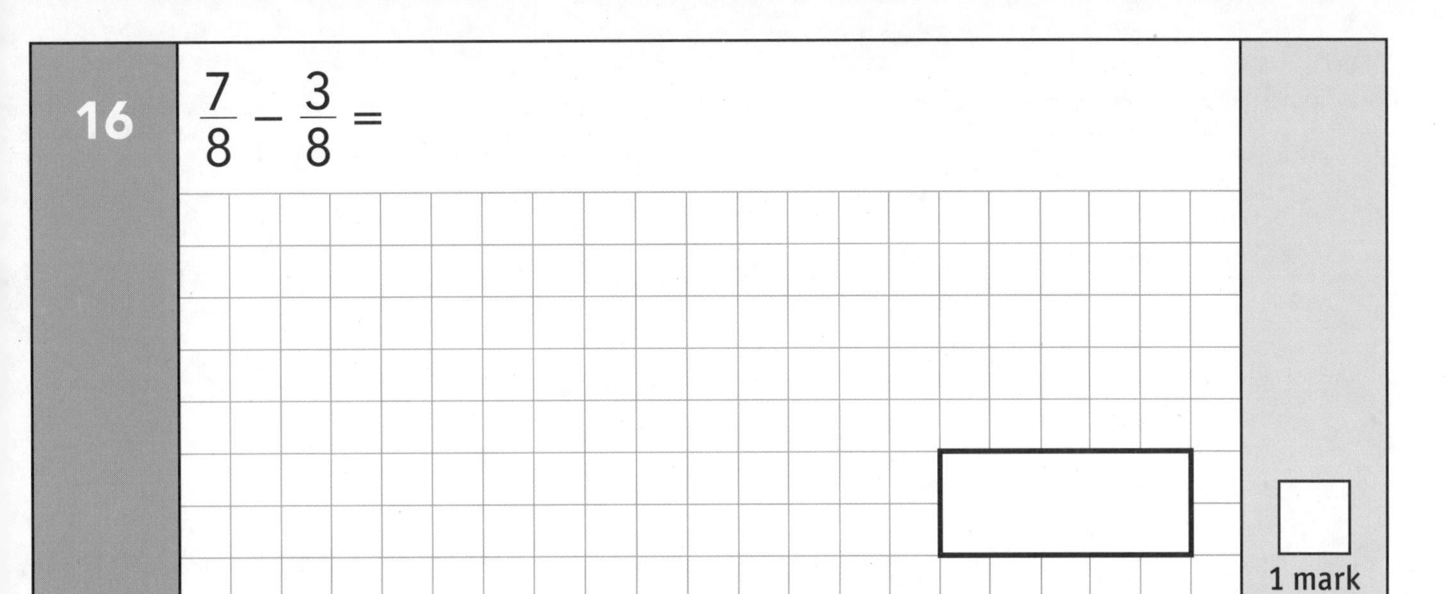

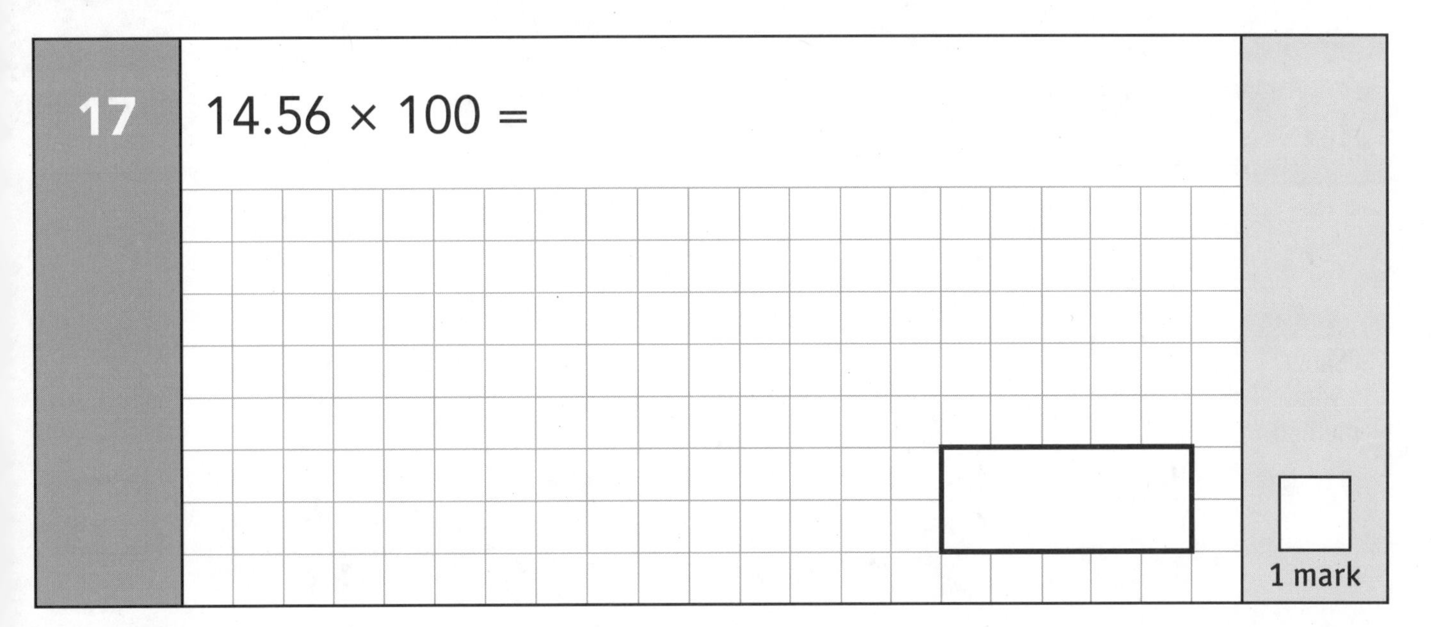

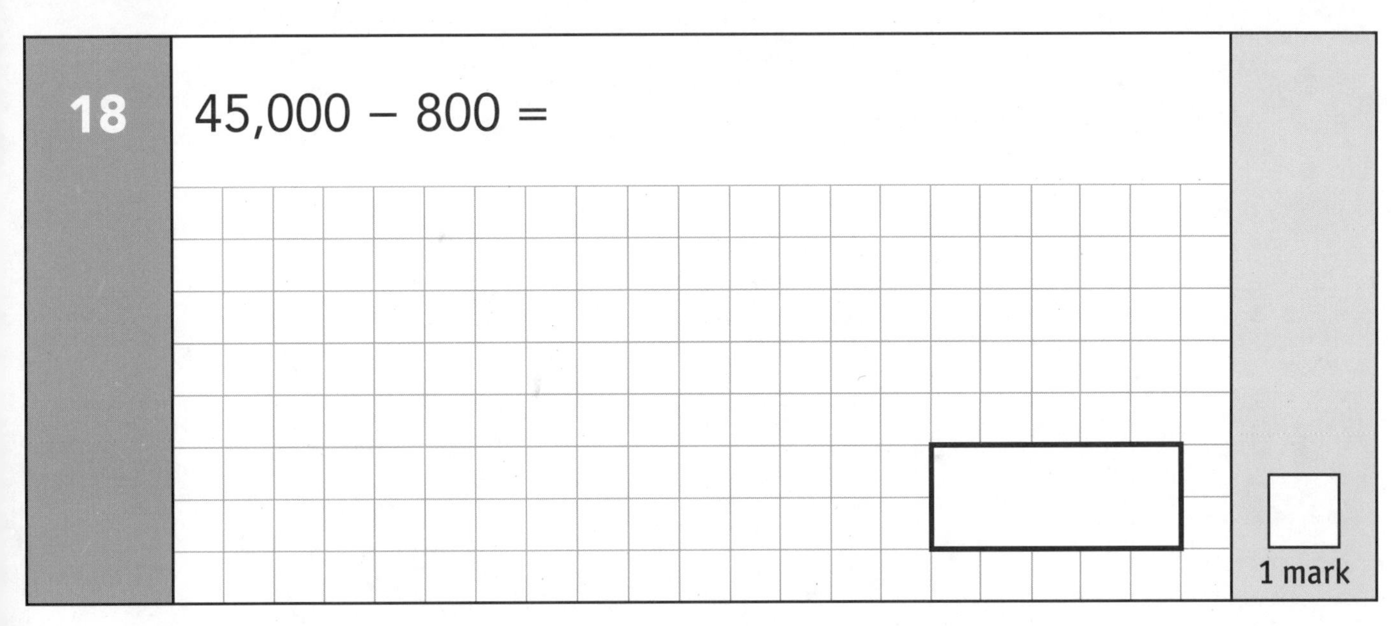

/3

Total for this page

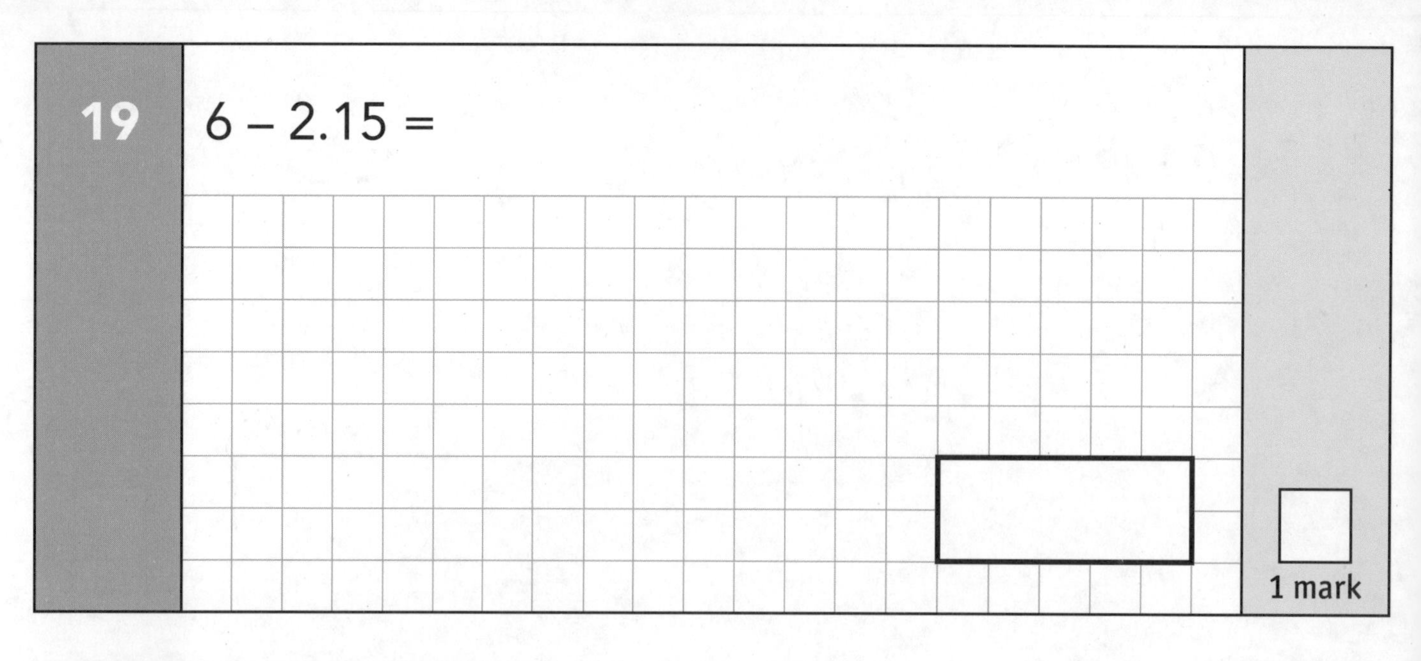

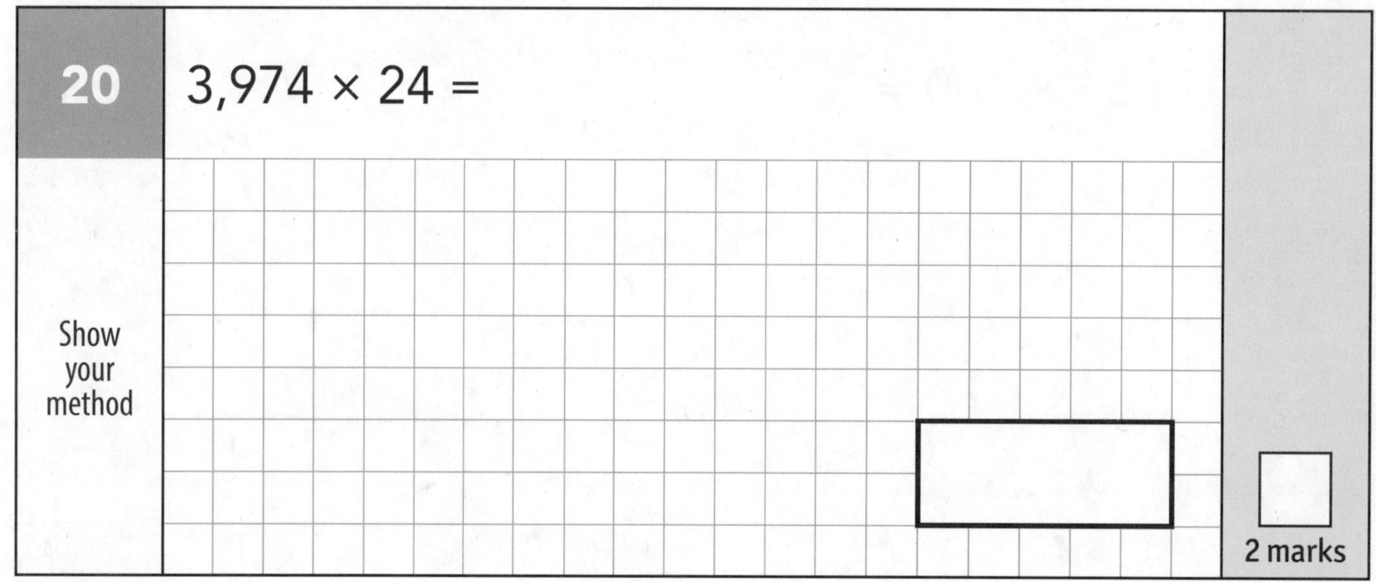

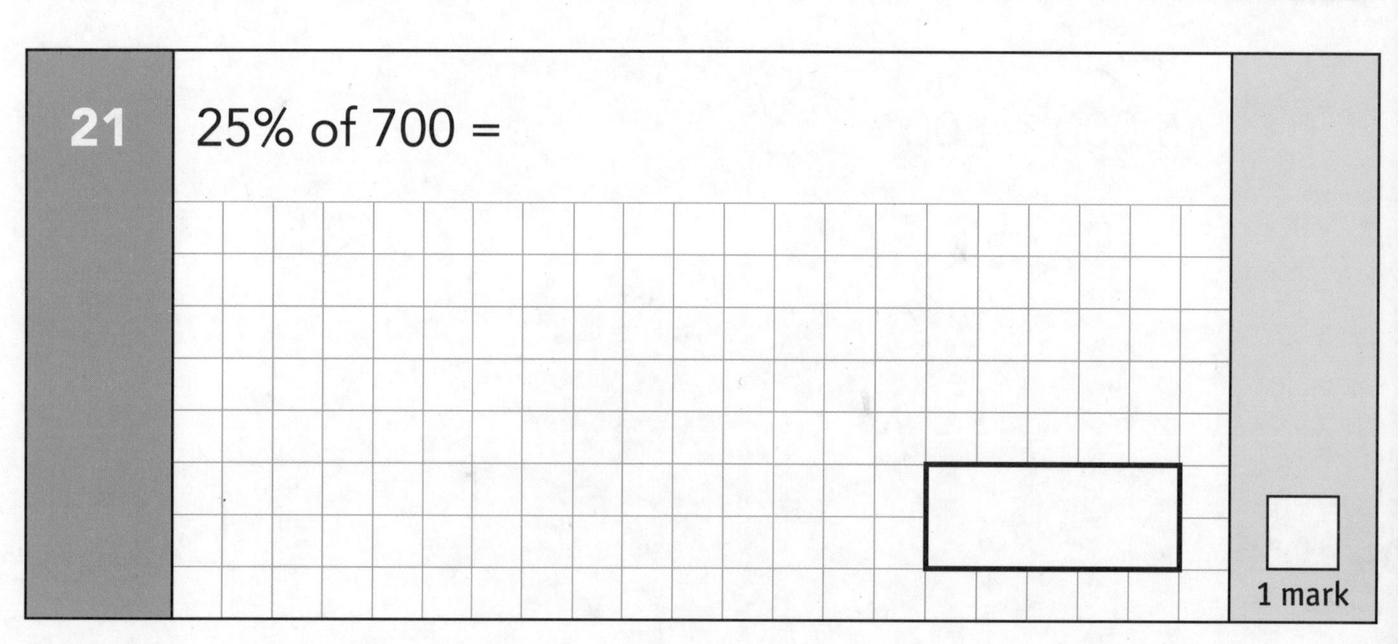

/4

Total for this page

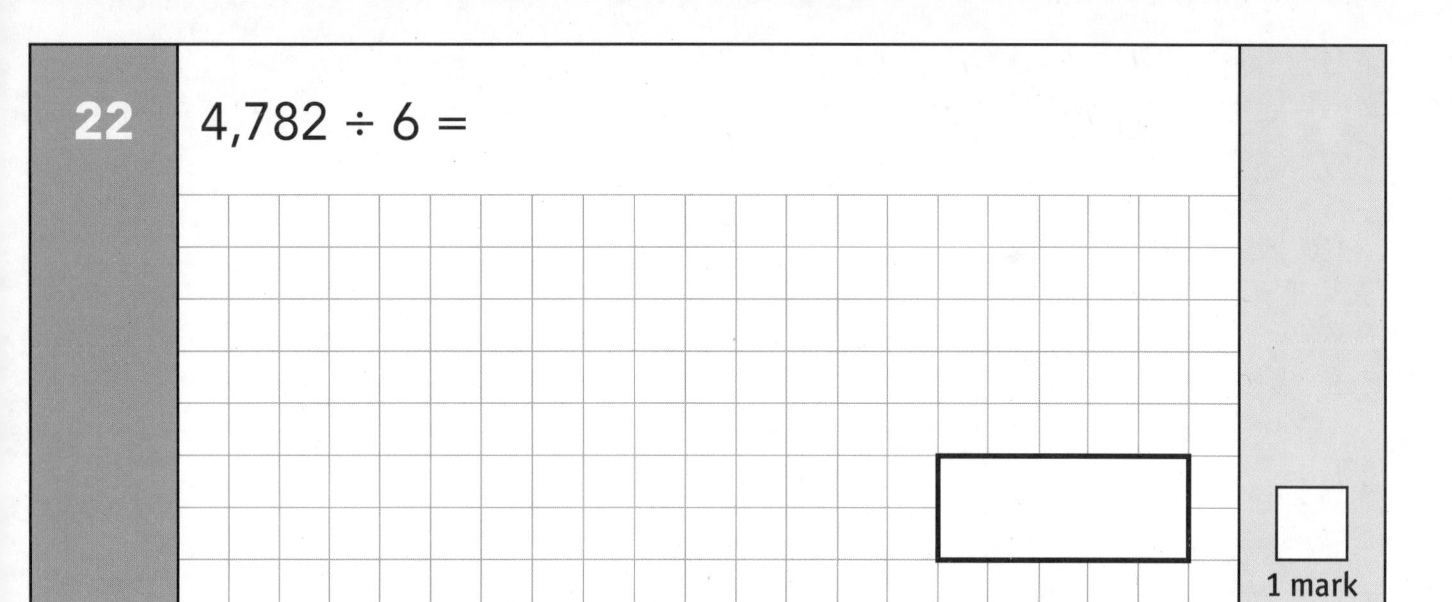

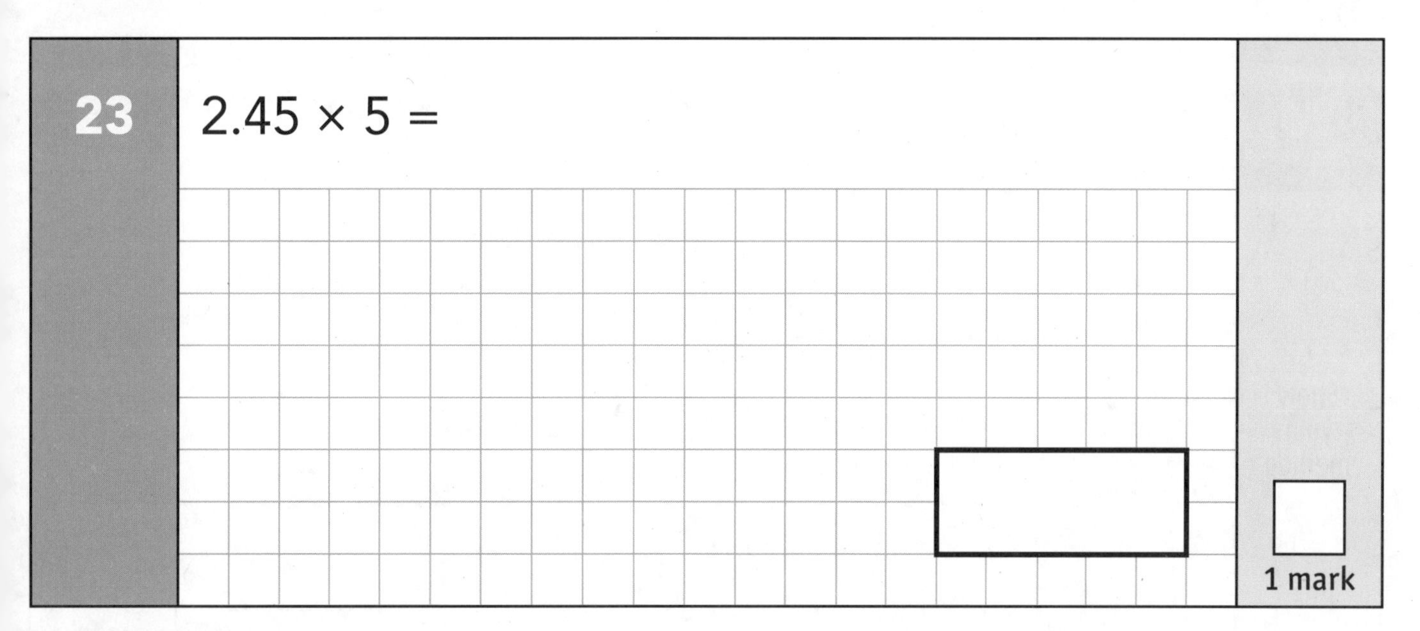

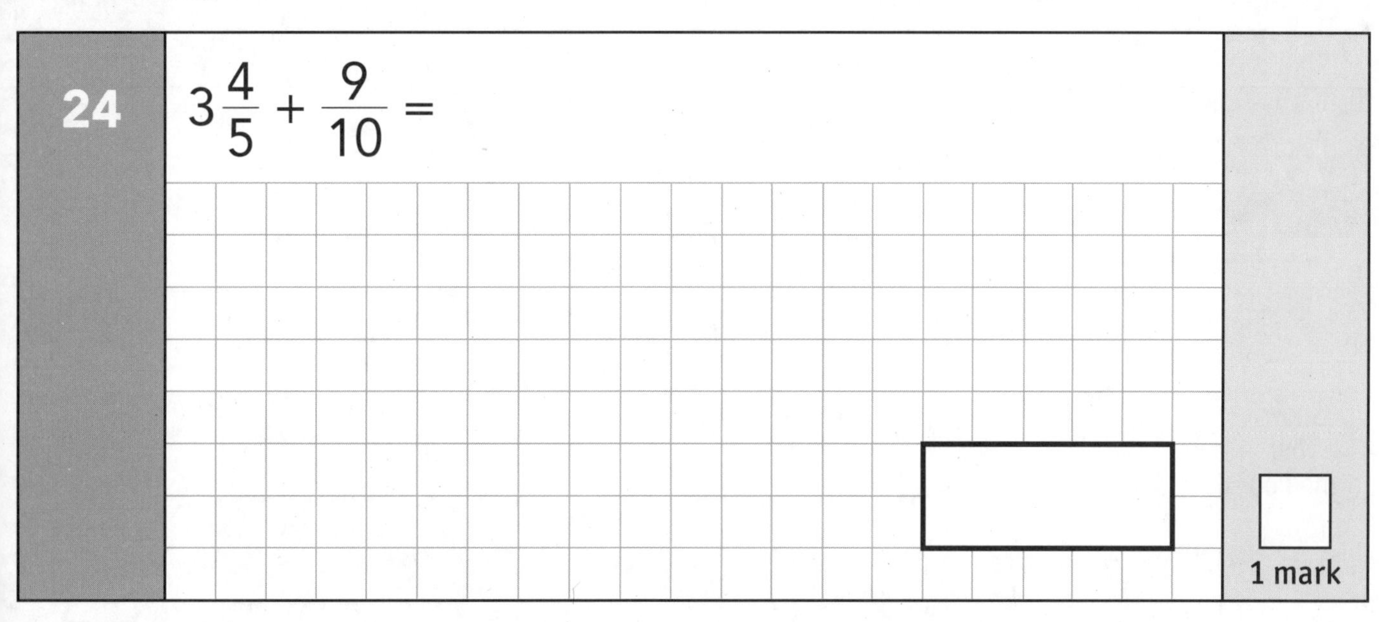

/3

Total for this page

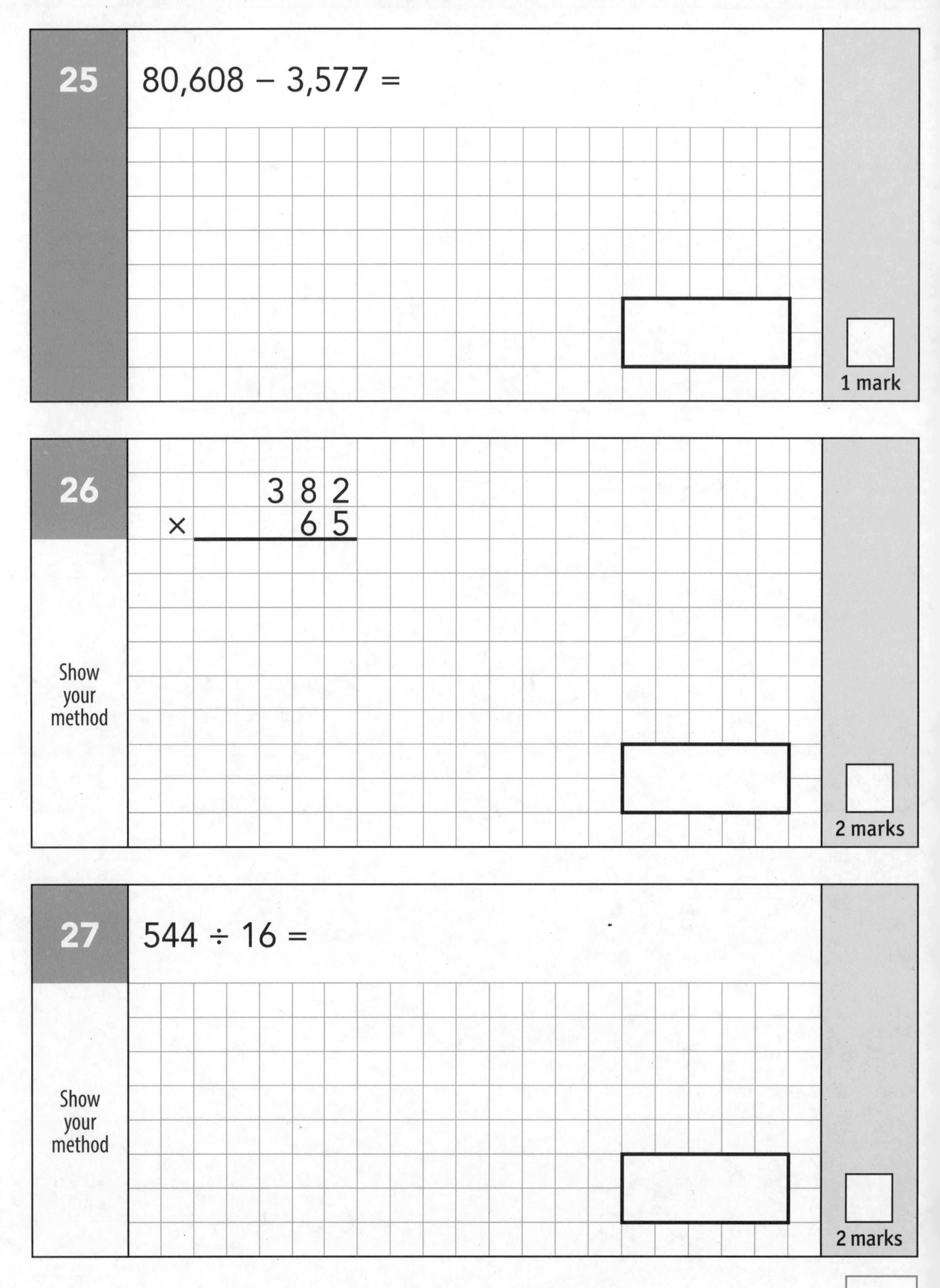

/5
Total for this page

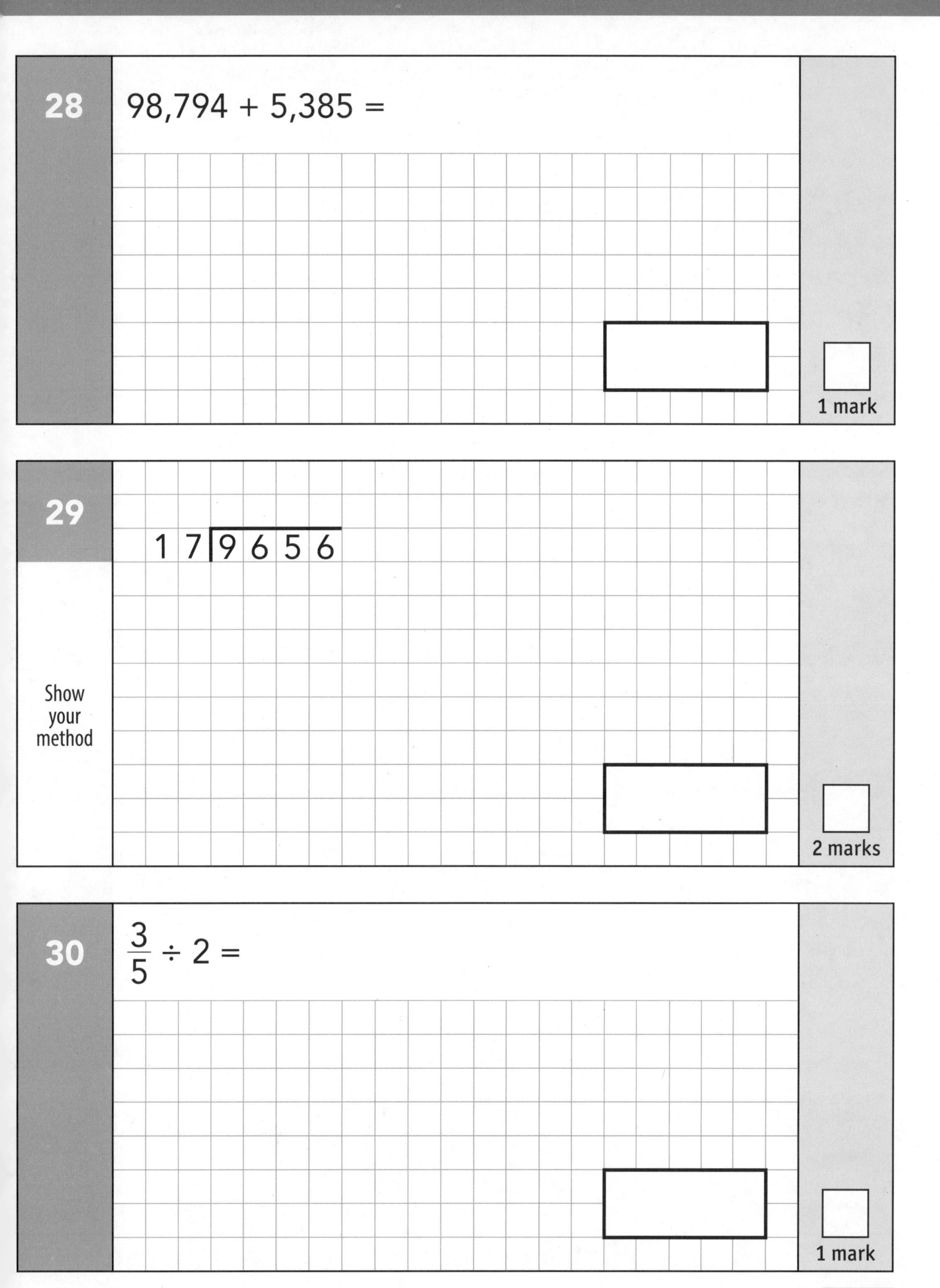

28 $98{,}794 + 5{,}385 =$

1 mark

29

$$17\overline{)9656}$$

Show your method

2 marks

30 $\frac{3}{5} \div 2 =$

1 mark

/4

Total for this page

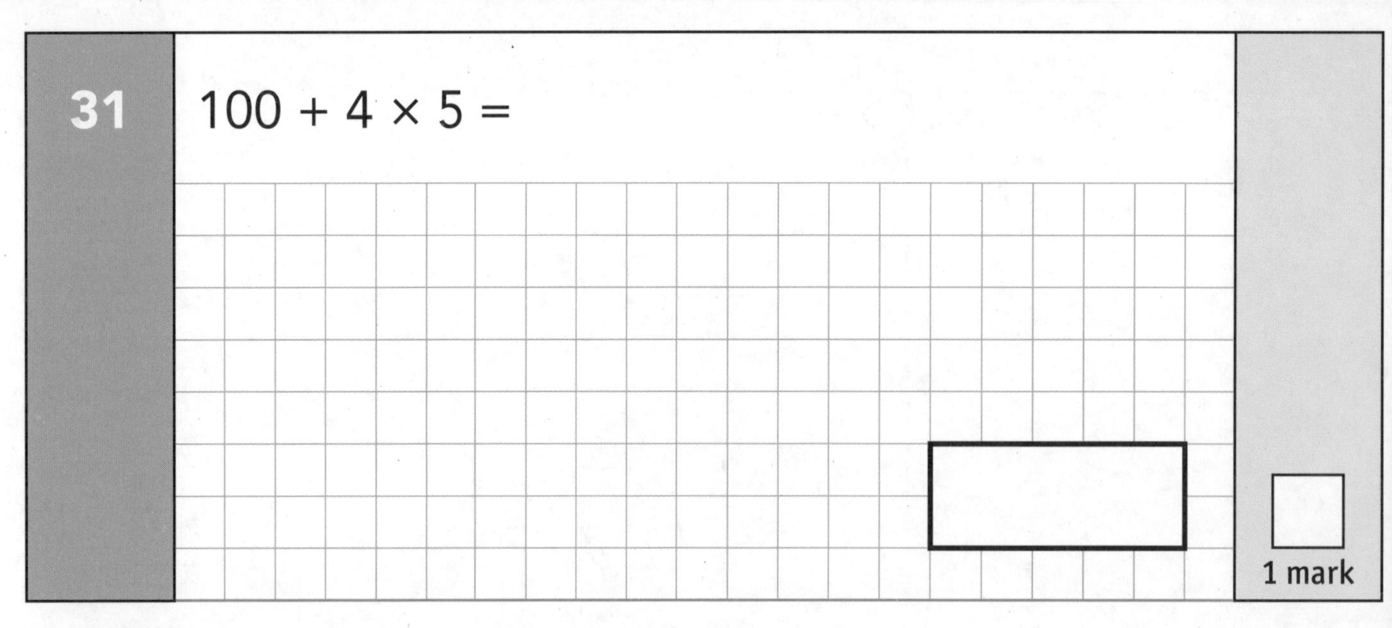

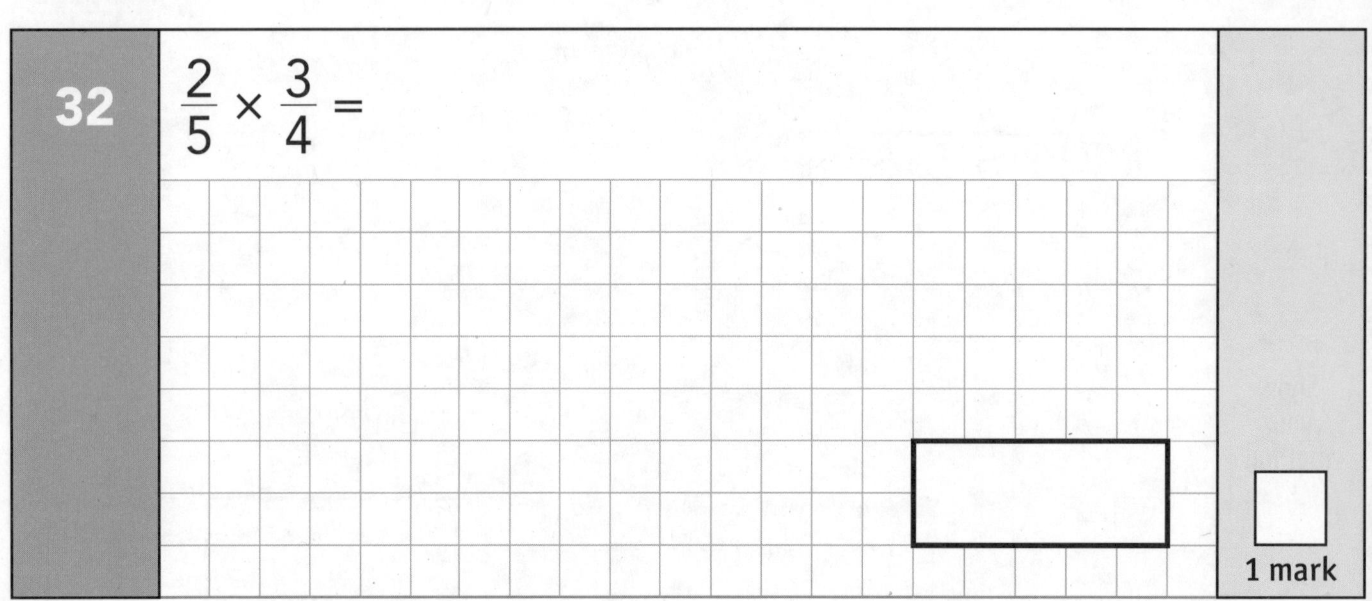

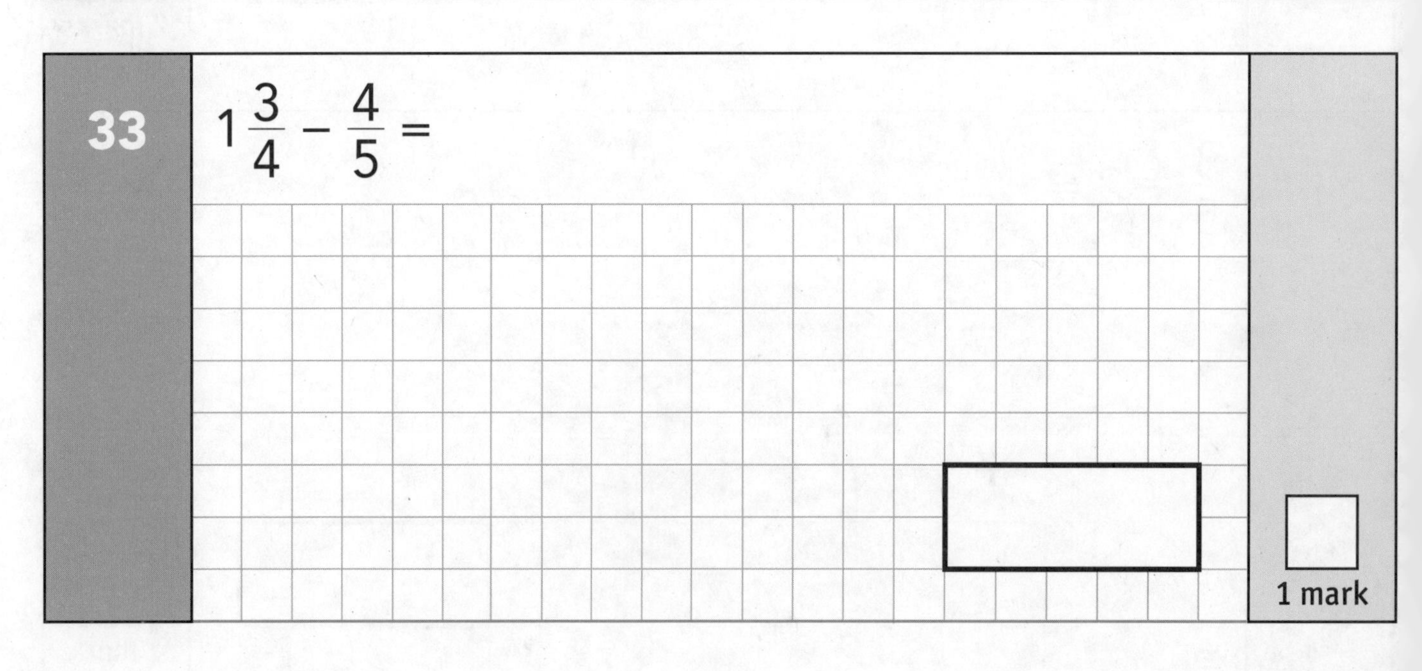

/3

Total for this page

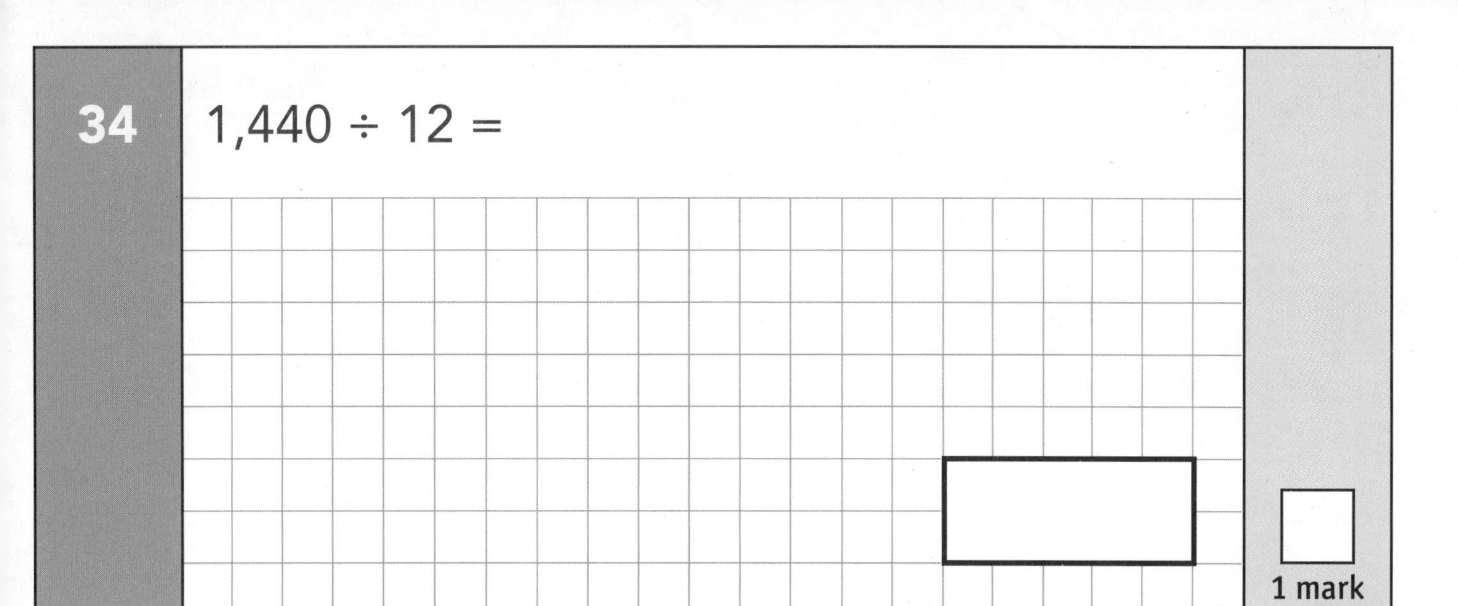

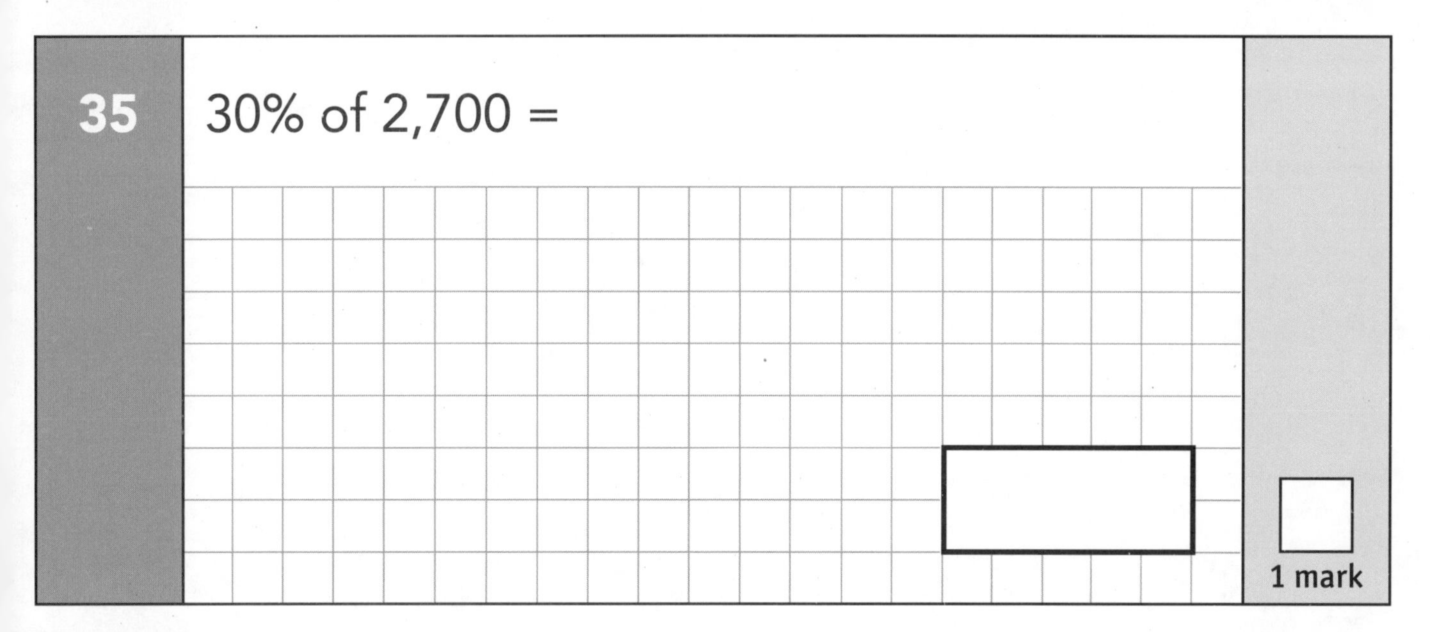

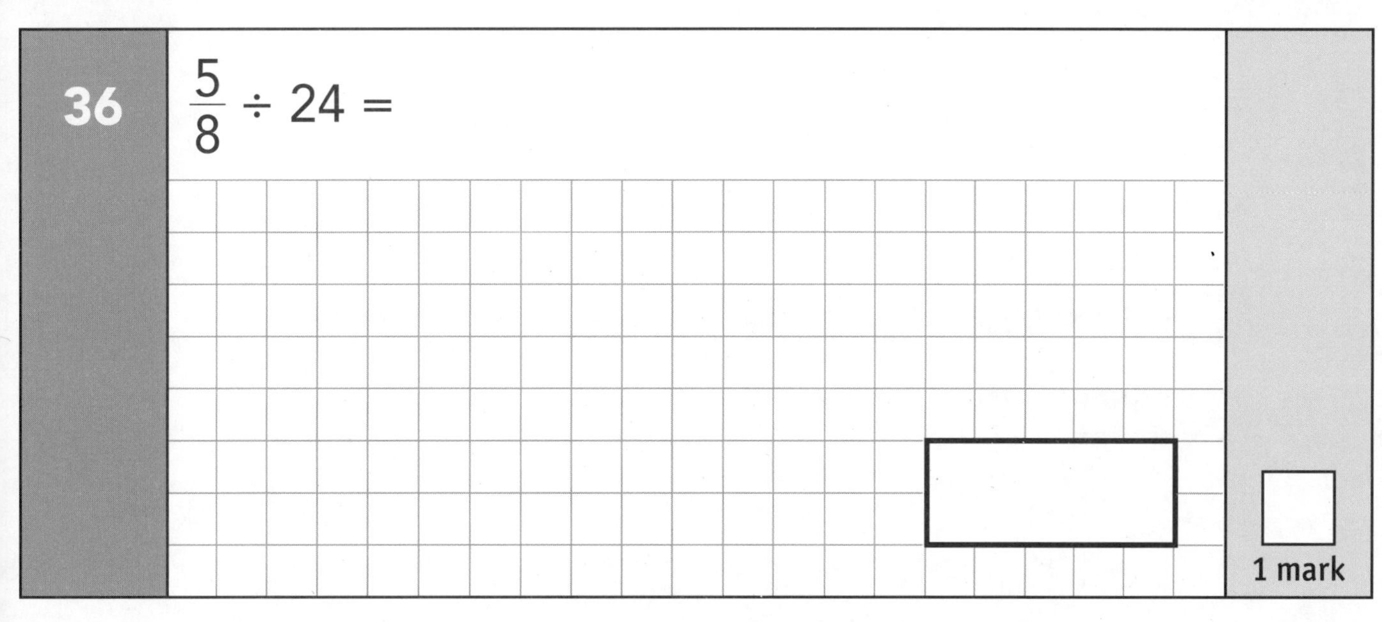

/3
Total for this page

Name:	Class:	Date:	Total marks: /35

Test 1, Paper 2: Reasoning

1 Circle **all** the prime numbers.

15 1 19 2 11 21

1 mark

2 Write the letters of the shapes in the correct position on the Carroll diagram.

	Fewer than 6 vertices	6 or more vertices
1 or more square faces		
No square faces		

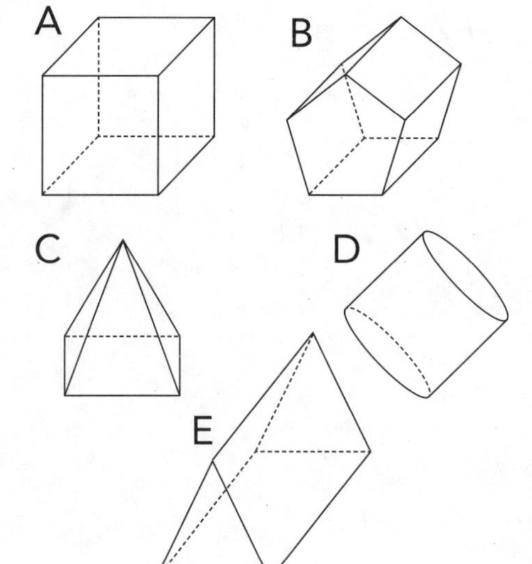

1 mark

3 Round **96,837**

to the nearest 10	
to the nearest 100	
to the nearest 1,000	

2 marks

/4

Total for this page

4 Here are four volumes.

3 litres   2,500 ml   5 litres   5,250 ml

Write the volumes in order, starting with the **least** amount.

______ ______ ______ ______

1 mark

5

8 cm

Not to scale

The perimeter of this rectangle is 70 cm.

Calculate the length of the rectangle.

[ ] cm

2 marks

6 Complete the table of equivalents.

Write fractions in their **simplest form**.

Fraction		$\frac{3}{5}$		$\frac{99}{100}$
Decimal	0.75			
Percentage			10%	99%

2 marks

/5

Total for this page

7

20					
25		35			
			48		
45					
		70			100

This is part of a multiplication square.

Fill in the four shaded boxes.

1 mark

8

Joseph's watering can holds 3 litres.

The watering can has a hole in it so he has to use a jug.

The jug holds 250 ml.

How many jugs of water does Joseph need to use to have the same amount of water as the watering can?

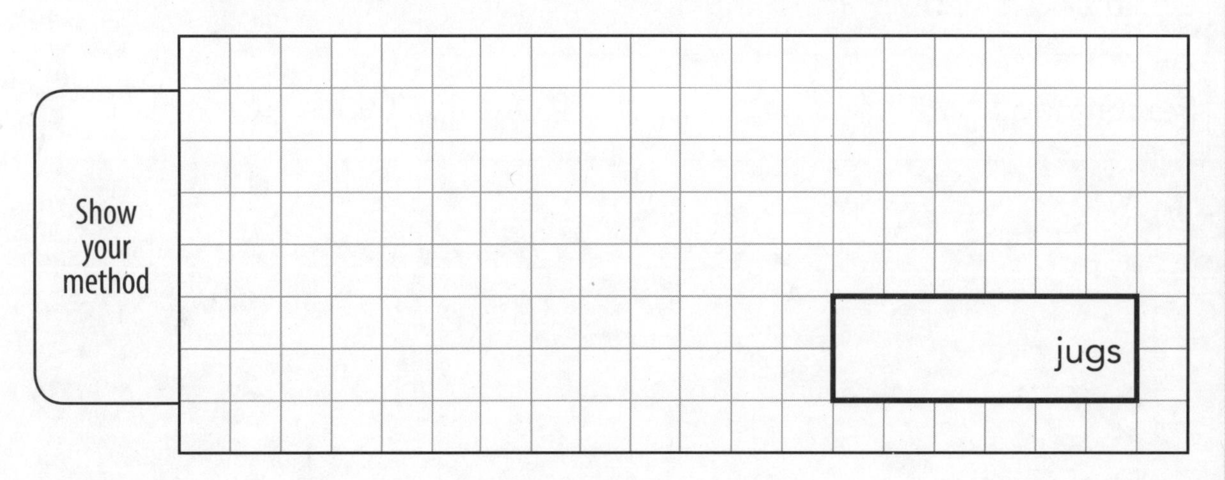

2 marks

/3

Total for this page

9

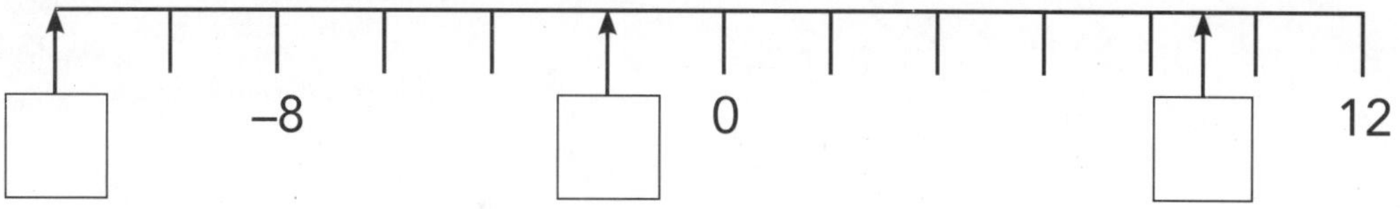

Fill in the empty boxes on the number line.

1 mark

10

Isaac wants to travel to Bruges by train.

He needs to arrive in Bruges by 6:30 p.m.

Circle the **latest time** that Isaac can leave London.

Leaves London	Arrives Bruges
14:01	16:31
14:50	17:20
15:35	18:05
15:55	18:25
16:01	18:31
18:35	21:05

1 mark

/2

Total for this page

11 There are 3,600 leaflets in a box.

Sarah and Jamie take 900 leaflets each.

Zoe and Xara share the rest of the leaflets equally.

How many leaflets does Zoe get?

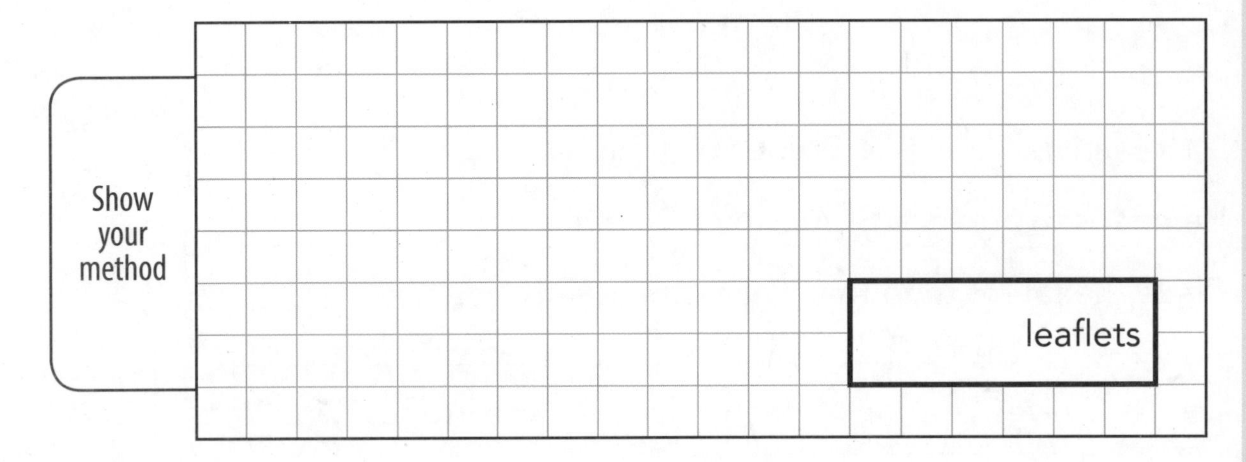

2 marks

12

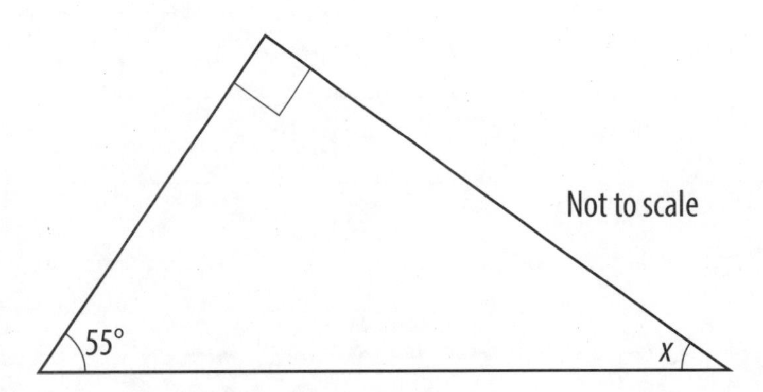

Calculate the size of **angle** x.

$x =$ ☐ °

1 mark

/3 *Total for this page*

13 Luke needs 750 g of pasta for a recipe.

How much will the pasta cost in total?

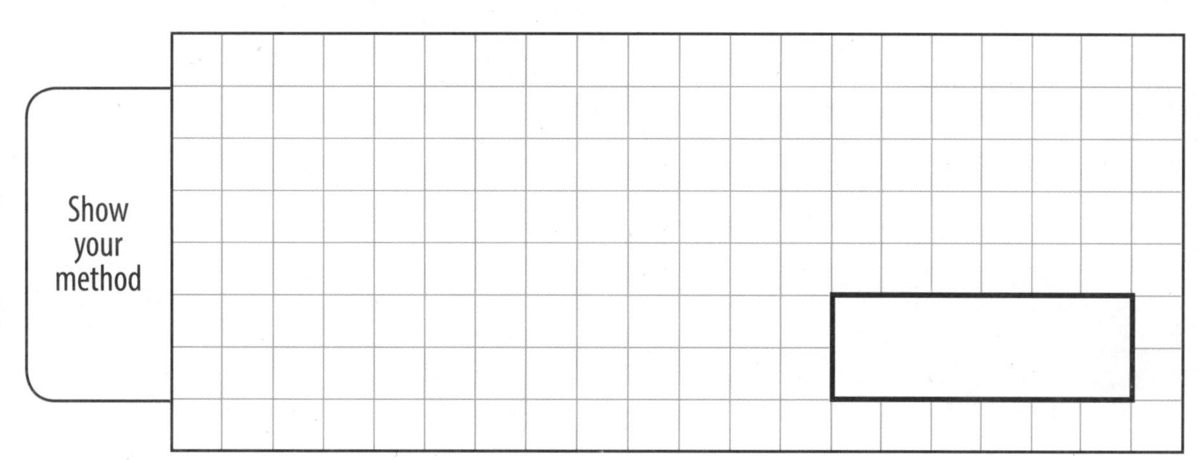

2 marks

14 Tick ✓ the **longest** period of time.

☐ $2\frac{3}{4}$ hours ☐ 170 minutes ☐ 2 hours 40 minutes

1 mark

/3

Total for this page

15 Anita chooses a number less than 9

She multiples it by 5 and then adds 5

She then divides this result by 7

Her answer is 5

What was the number she started with? ☐

2 marks

16 The shaded squares represent a mixed number.

Write the mixed number.

Then write it as an improper fraction.

mixed number ☐ improper fraction ☐

1 mark

17

Kayleigh thinks of a 3-D shape.

She says:

"It has 6 faces.

All the faces are equal.

All the faces are square."

What is the name of the 3-D shape? ☐

1 mark

/4

Total for this page

18 Here is a number written in Roman numerals.

LXIV

Write the number in figures. ☐

1 mark

19 a) Ben says: "2.22 is larger than 2.42"

Explain why he is incorrect.

1 mark

b) Draw lines to match each fraction to the correct decimal.

The first one has been done for you.

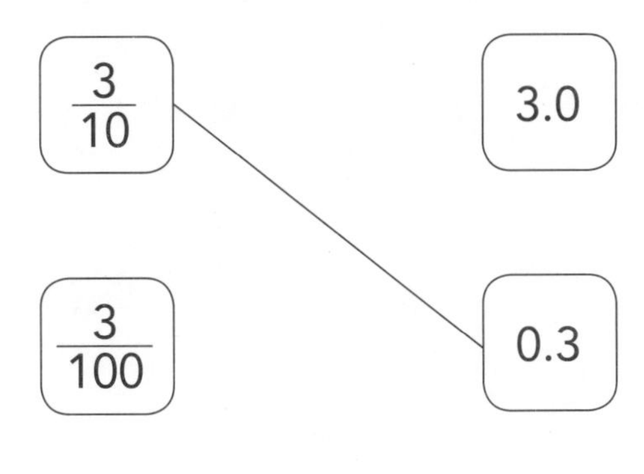

1 mark

/3

Total for this page

20 The line graph shows how the water level in a small river changes.

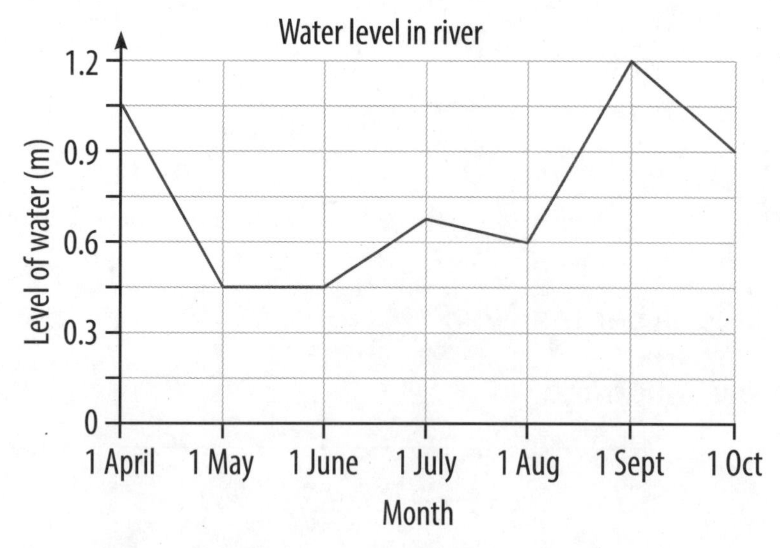

a) Between which **two** dates did the water level stay the **same**?

____________ and ____________

1 mark

b) How much **lower** was the water level on 1 June than on 1 July?

m

1 mark

21 Here is a pattern of number pairs.

a	b
1	7
2	17
3	27
4	37

Write a rule to find **b**.

1 mark

/3

Total for this page

22 Jo thinks of a mystery number.

She divides it by 100 and then finds one-fifth.

Her new number is 0.4

What was Jo's mystery number? ☐

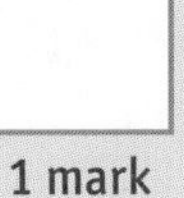

1 mark

23 Use the formula $A = \frac{1}{2}$ (base × height) to calculate the area of this triangle.

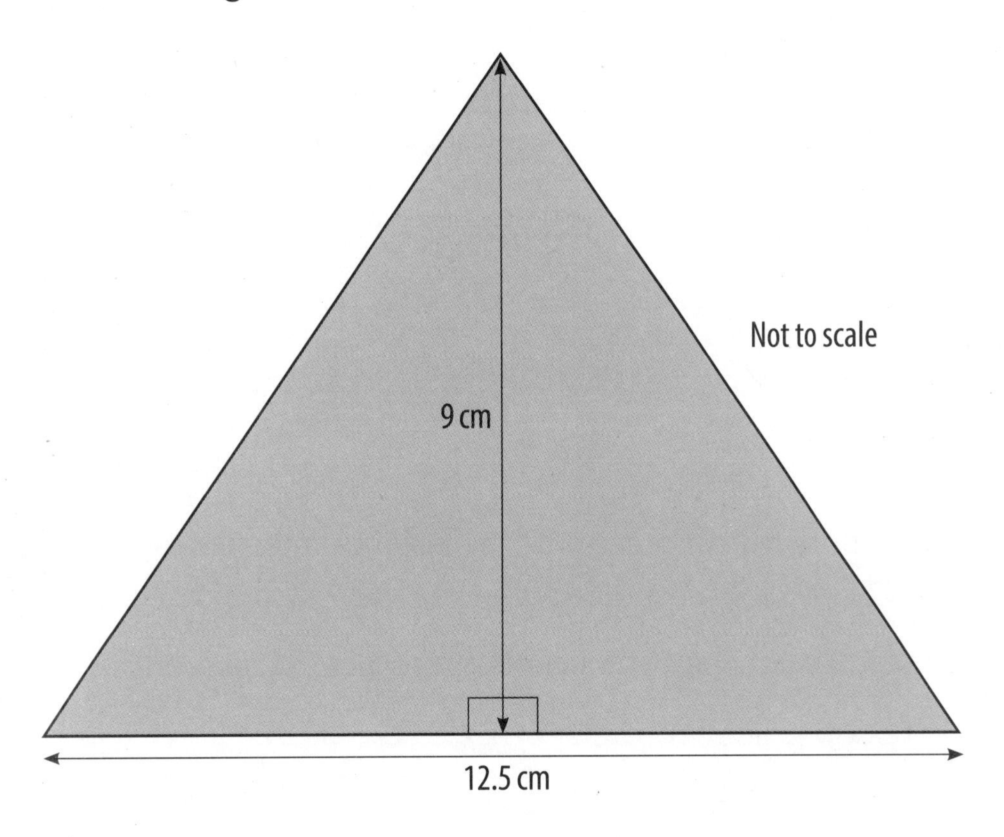

☐ cm^2

1 mark

/2

Total for this page

24 This is part of a train timetable.

Little Brook	11:37	12:12	12:37	13:12
Great Hills	12:51	12:55	13:51	13:55
Lower Vales	–	13:24	–	14:24

Jenna lives in Little Brook.

She has a meeting in Lower Vales at 2:45 p.m.

> The latest train I can take from Little Brook is at 12:12

Is Jenna correct? Circle your answer. YES / NO

Explain your answer.

1 mark

25 In a competition, Ben scores $\frac{3}{5}$ of the total points scored by Jules.

Jules scores 50% of the total points scored by Razia.

Razia scores 60 points in total.

Calculate the total points **Ben** scores.

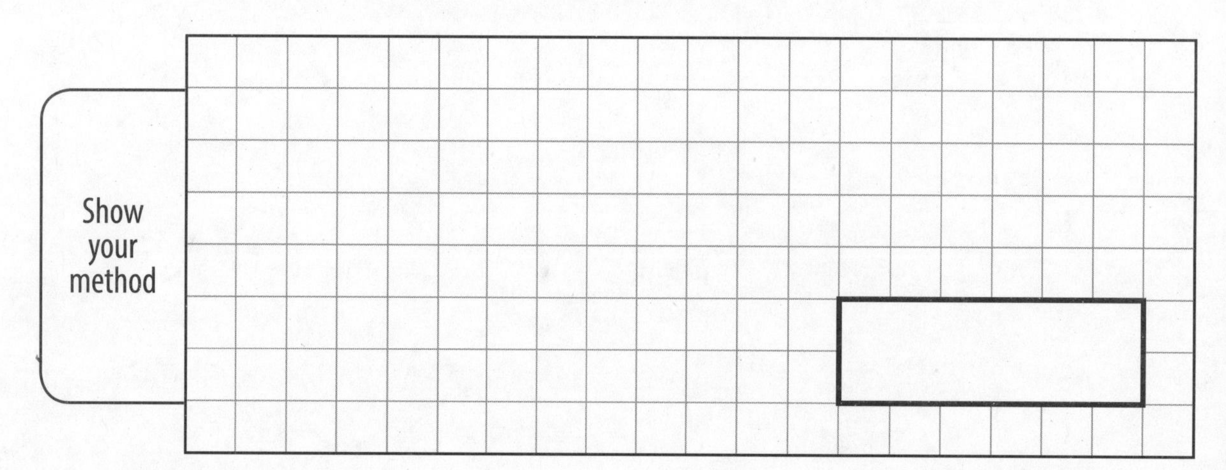

2 marks

/3 Total for this page

Name:	Class:	Date:	Total marks: /35

Test 1, Paper 3: Reasoning

1 Write the missing numbers.

One has been done for you.

50 —is 60 less than→ 110

[ ] —is 60 less than→ 230

150 —is 60 less than→ [ ]

1 mark

2 Circle the numbers that are **3 more** than a **multiple of 5**

125 87 53 28 100

1 mark

3 Write the missing signs <, > or = in each box to make these statements **true**.

45×10 [ ] $4{,}500 \div 10$

$450 \div 100$ [ ] $0.45 \times 1{,}000$

0.45×100 [ ] $4{,}500 \div 1{,}000$

1 mark

/3

Total for this page

4 A pack of paper has 120 sheets.

6 children each take 5 sheets.

How many sheets of paper are left in the packet?

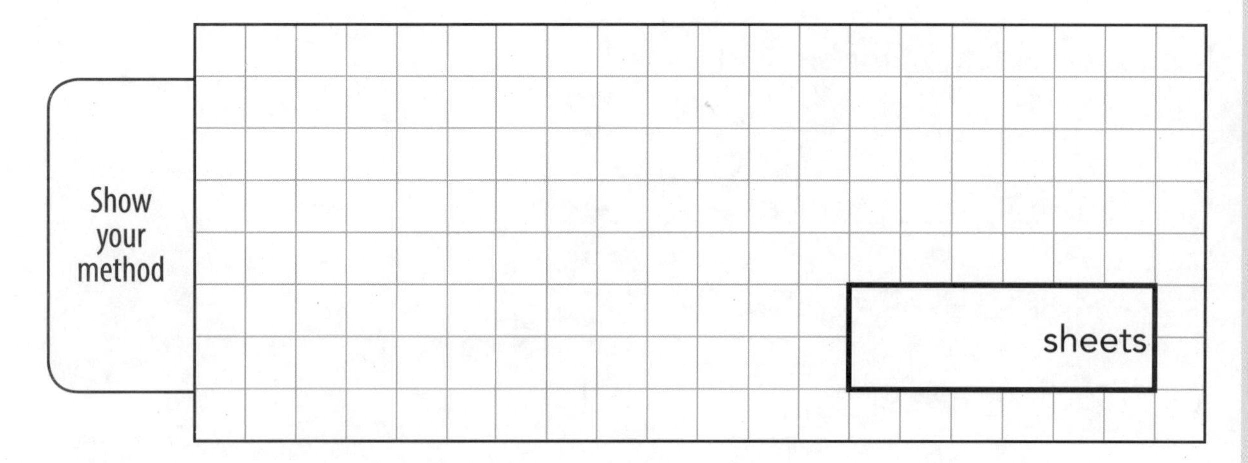

2 marks

5 Write in the missing numbers.

Number	Rounded to the nearest **whole** number
8.05	
8.55	
8.45	
8.54	

2 marks

6

Put these cars in order of price, starting with the **highest price**.

One has been done for you.

_____ C _____ _____ _____

highest **lowest**

2 marks

/6

Total for this page

7 Draw a square with **half the area** of this rectangle.

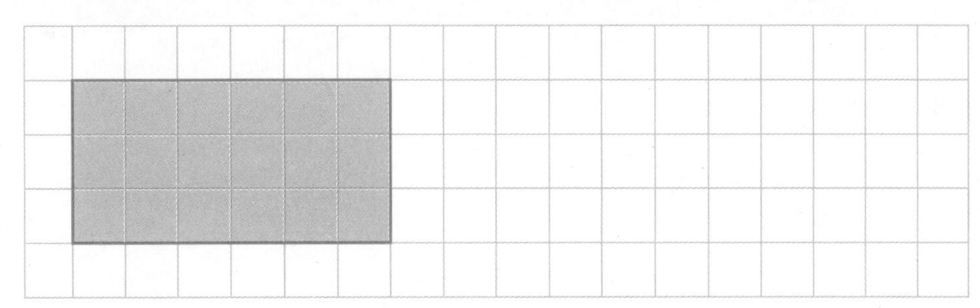

1 mark

8 Complete the number sequence and write the rule.

1,350 1,750 ☐ 2,550

The rule is ____________________

1 mark

9 Tick the statements that are **true**.

$\frac{1}{5}$ of 200 = 50 ☐

2,000 ÷ 8 = 250 ☐

25% of 2,000 = 500 ☐

1 mark

10 Write the missing numbers to make this **multiplication** grid correct.

×	☐	☐
4	28	48
☐	56	96

2 marks

/5

Total for this page

11 The numbers in this sequence increase by the same amount each time.

Write the missing numbers.

	$1\frac{3}{7}$	$1\frac{6}{7}$	$2\frac{2}{7}$	

2 marks

12 A box of 6 tins of tomato soup costs £4.80

A box of 4 tins of the same tomato soup costs £3.60

What is the difference in the cost of 1 tin between the two boxes?

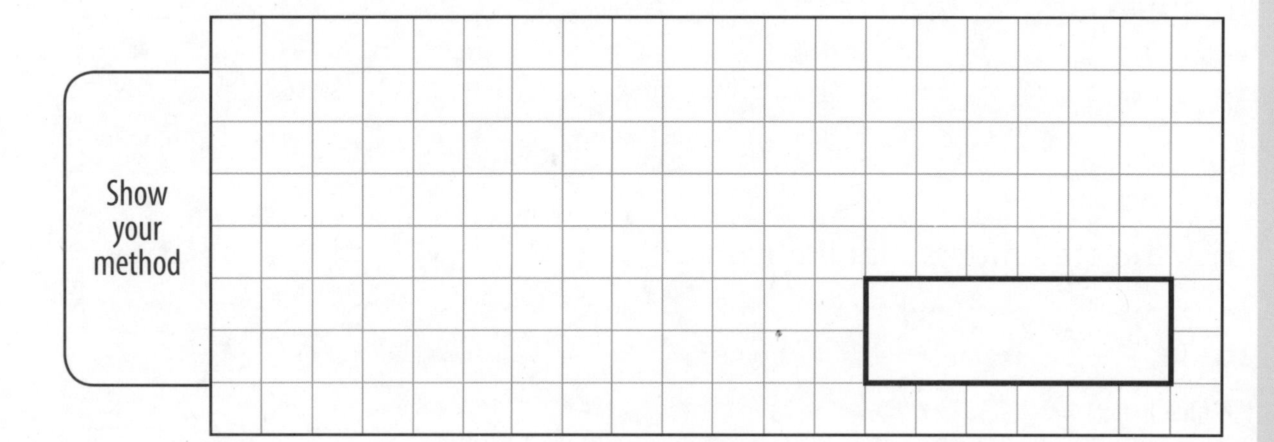

2 marks

/4

Total for this page

13 Calculate the size of angles *a* and *b*.

a = ☐ °

b = ☐ °

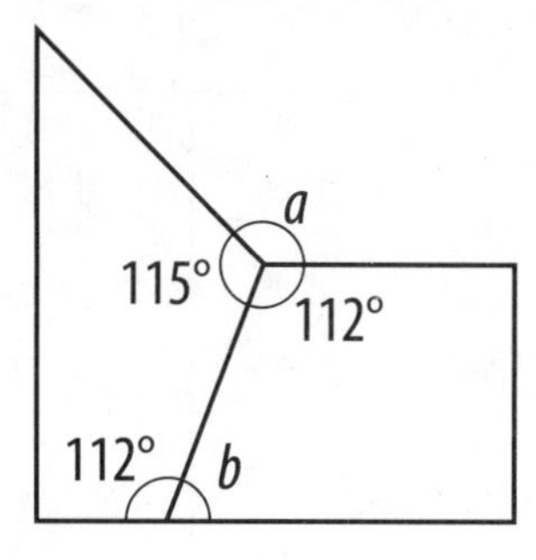

2 marks

14 Jay picks five number cards from a pile.

20 5 12 7 16

a) Calculate the **mean** of Jay's numbers. ☐

1 mark

b) Jay picks another number card from the pile.

The mean of the six numbers is **one more** than before.

What other number did Jay pick? ☐

1 mark

15 Write the missing digits to make this addition correct.

	3	0	☐	7
+	1	☐	3	☐
	4	5	2	0

1 mark

/5

Total for this page

16 A shop sells pairs of gloves for winter.

Patterned gloves
1 pair for £6.50

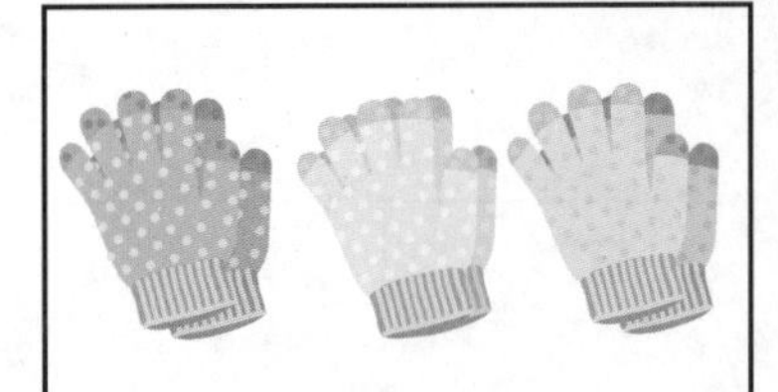

Dotted gloves
3 pairs for £8.75

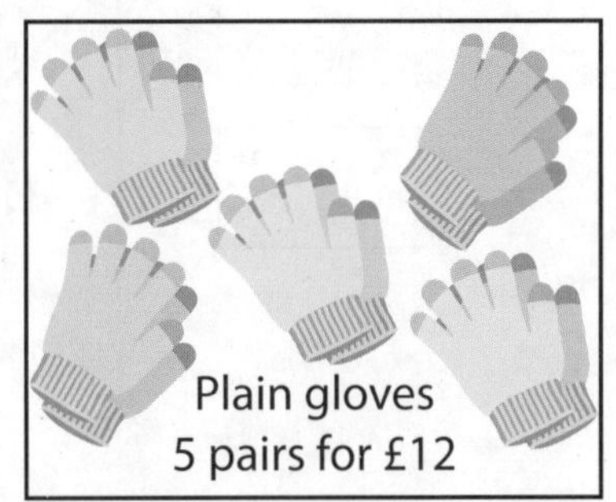

Plain gloves
5 pairs for £12

Olivia buys 1 pair of patterned gloves for herself and 3 pairs of dotted gloves for her children.

She gives the shopkeeper £20

How much change does she get?

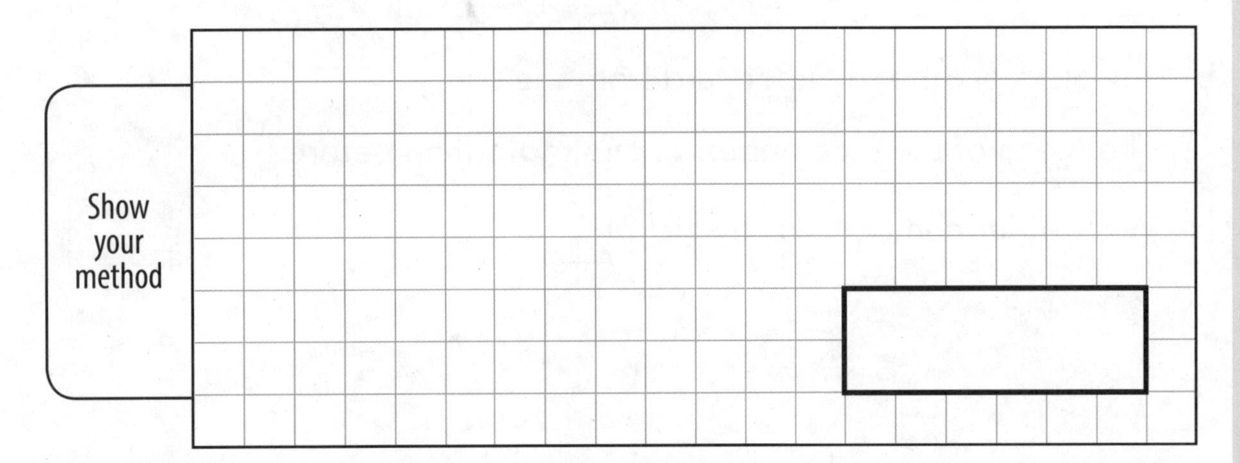

2 marks

/2

Total for this page

17 Four children make paper chains for a party.

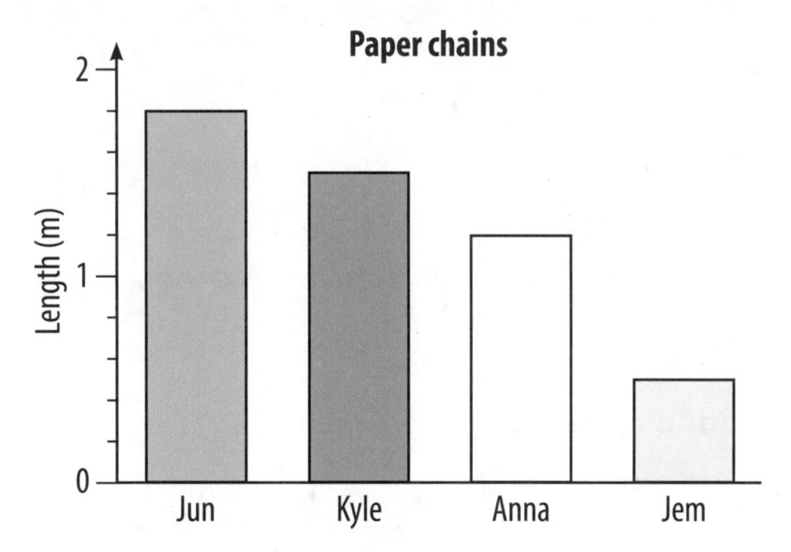

a) Complete the table.

	Jun	Kyle	Anna	Jem
Length (m)				

1 mark

b) Kyle cuts his paper chain into five equal pieces.

What is the length of each piece? [ ] m

1 mark

18 The clock shows the time that Kayla and Jon parked their cars at the fair.

Car park 45p for 20 minutes

I left the fair at 16:30; Jon left the fair only 5 minutes before me but he paid 45p less.

Explain why this happened.

2 marks

/4 *Total for this page*

19 25% of Izzy's number is 100

What is 20% of Izzy's number? [ ]

2 marks

20 Amelie is one and a half metres shorter than her mother.

Amelie's mother is 200 cm tall.

Amelie's brother is **double** the height of Amelie.

What is the height of Amelie's brother? [ ] cm

1 mark

21 Calculate the **difference** in volume between the cuboid and the cube.

7 cm

15 cm

6 cm

7 cm

Not to scale

Show your method

[ ] cm^3

3 marks

/6

Total for this page

Name:	Class:	Date:	Total marks: /40

Test 2, Paper 1: Arithmetic

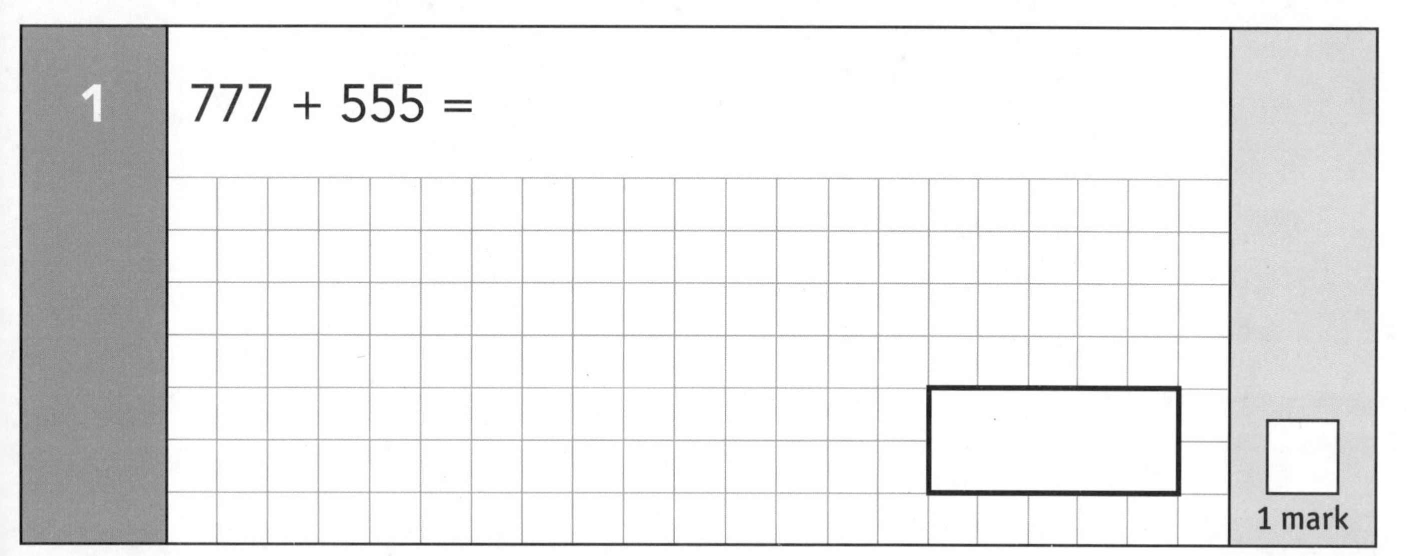

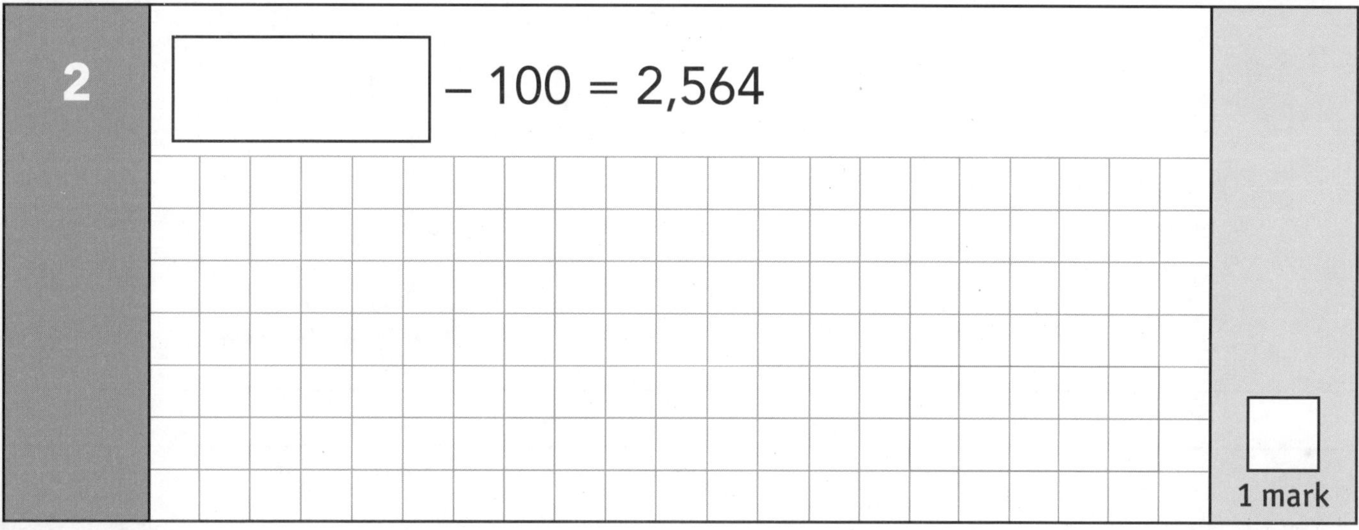

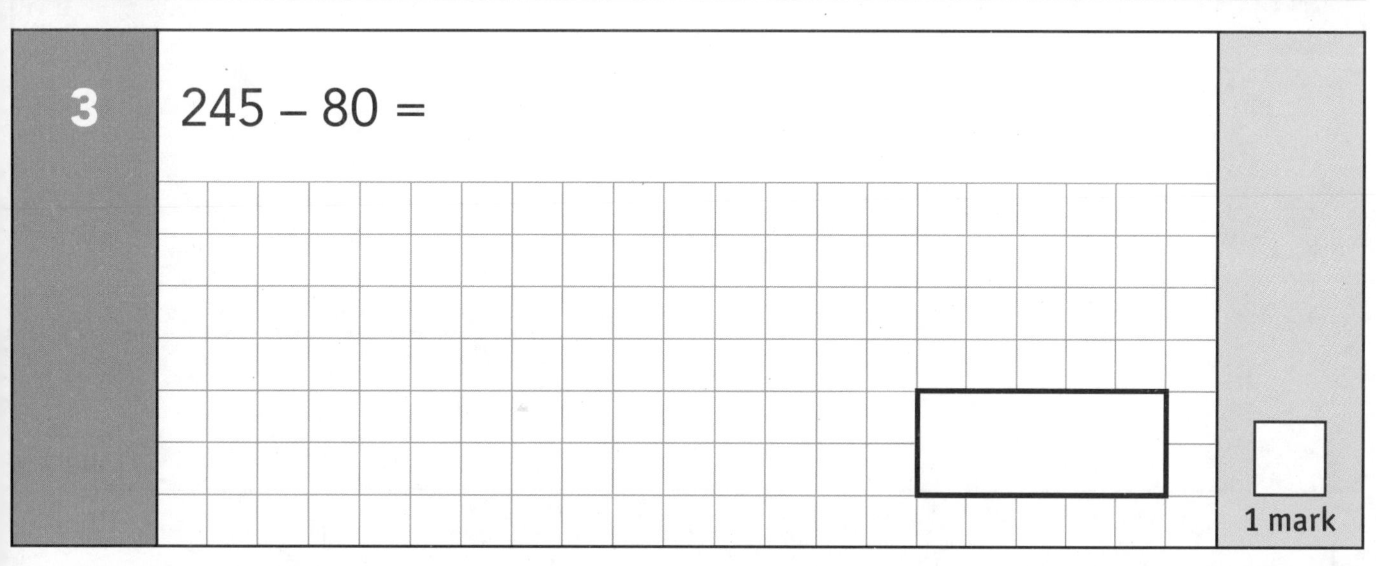

/2

Total for this page

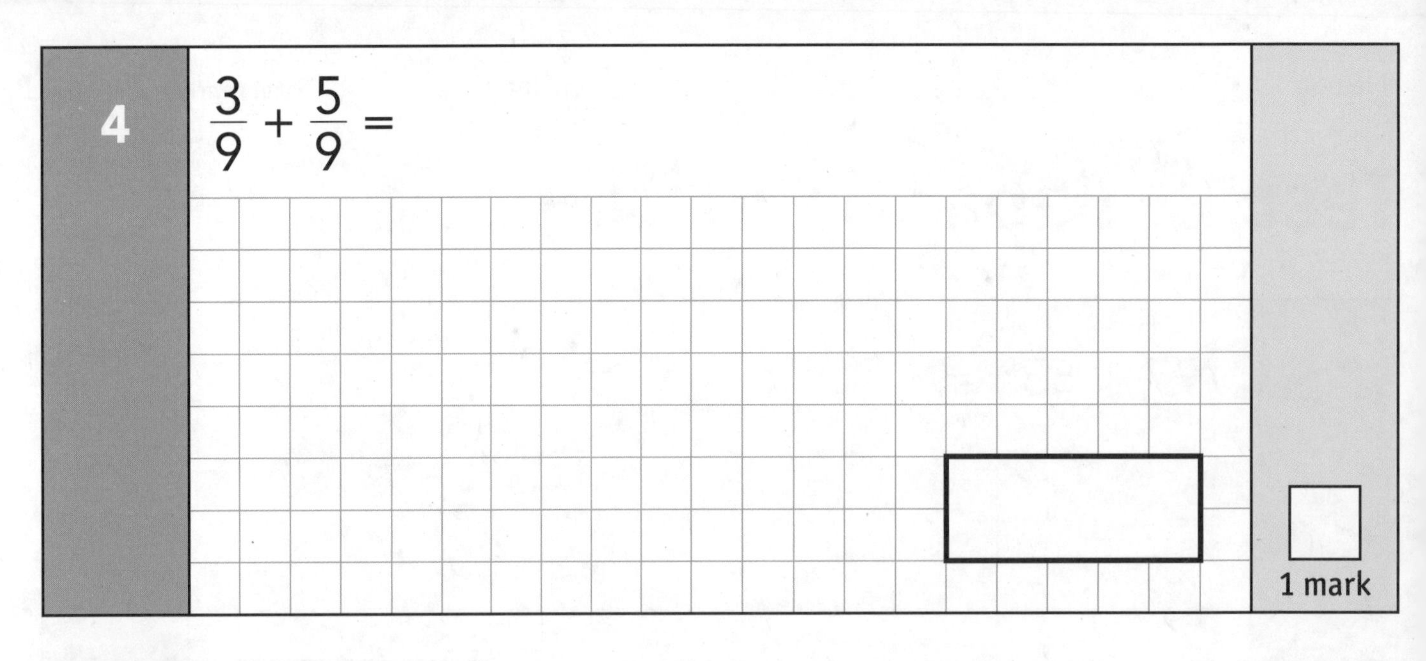

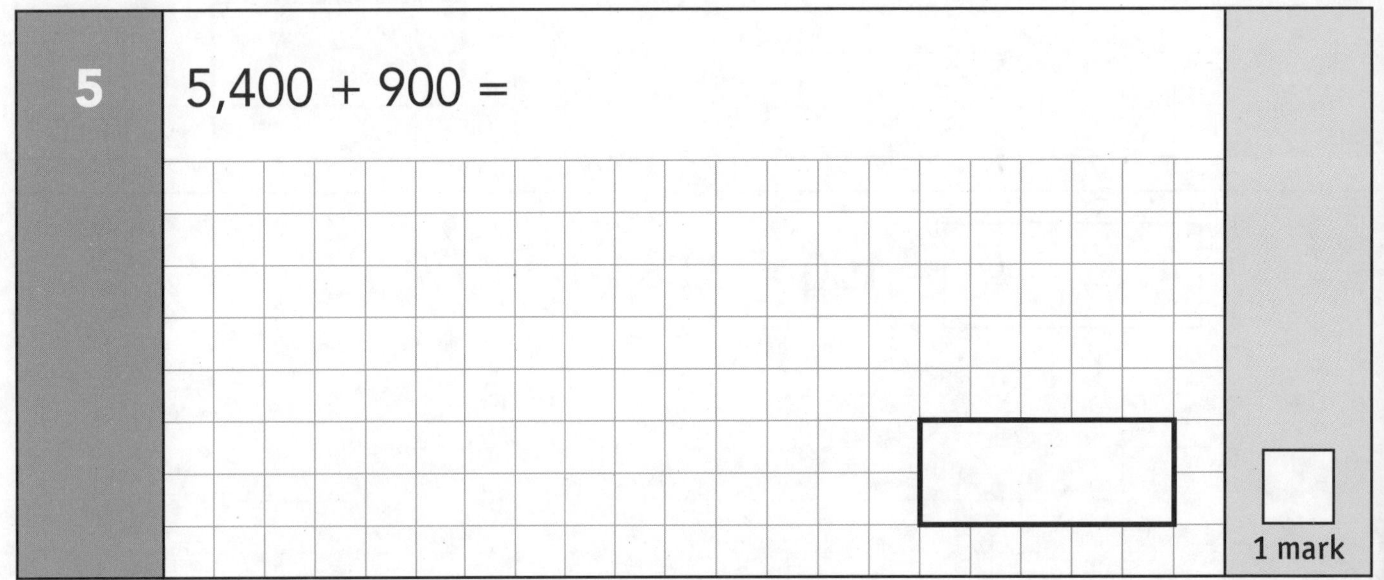

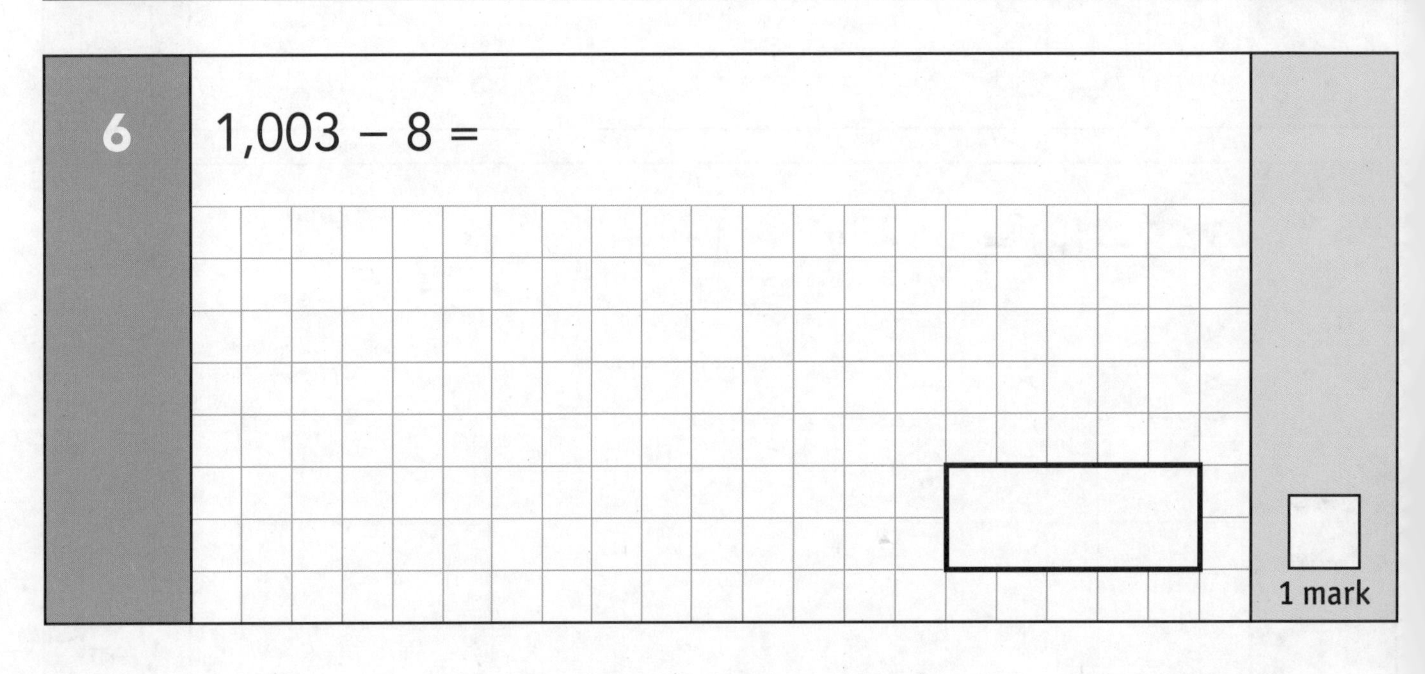

/3

Total for this page

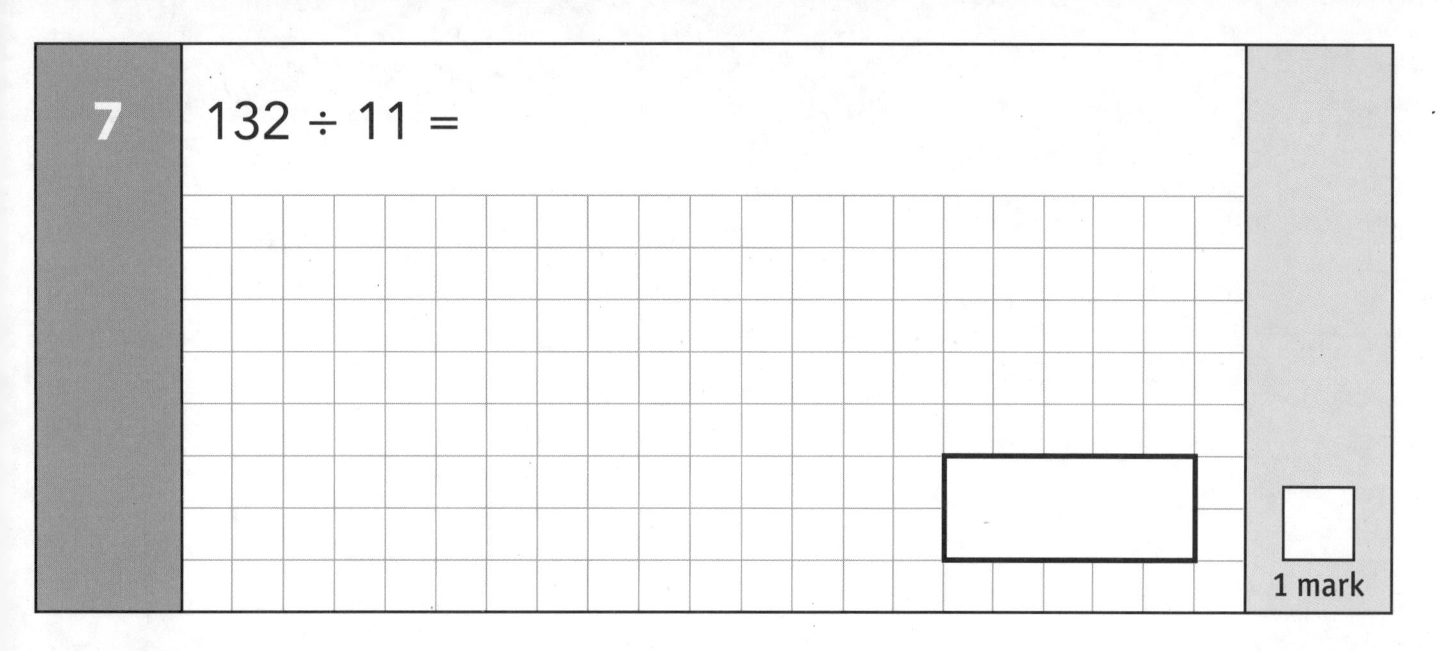

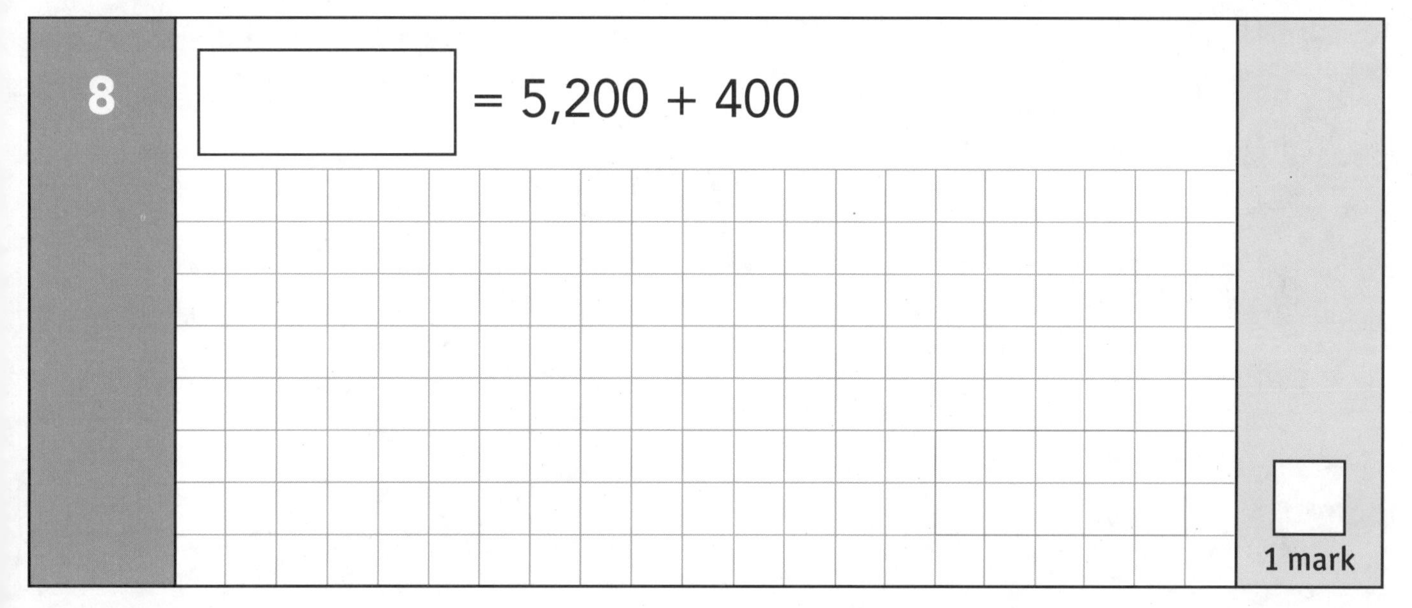

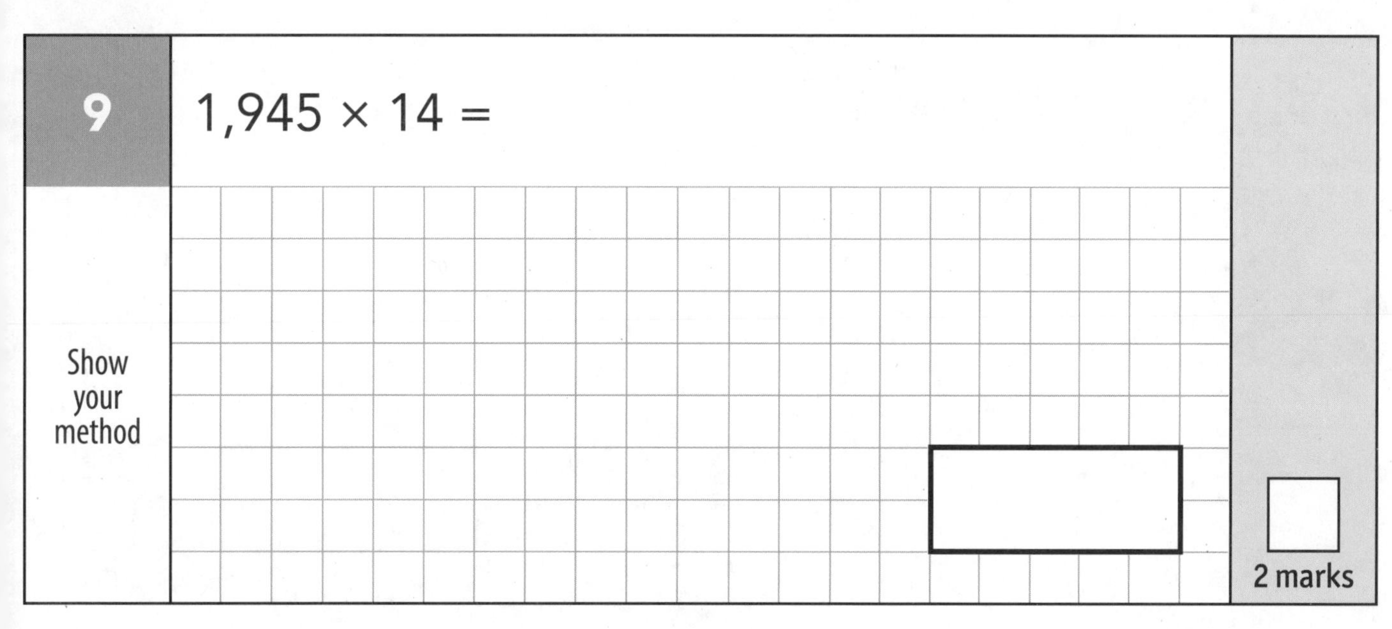

/3

Total for this page

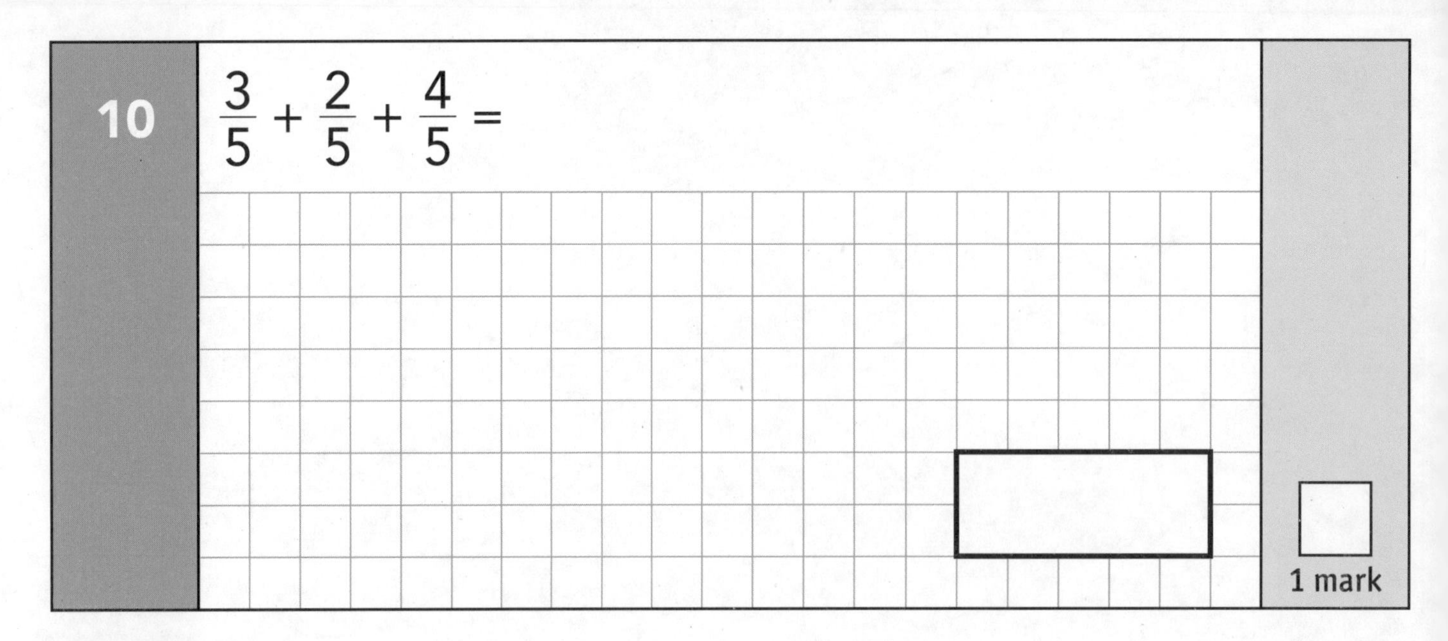

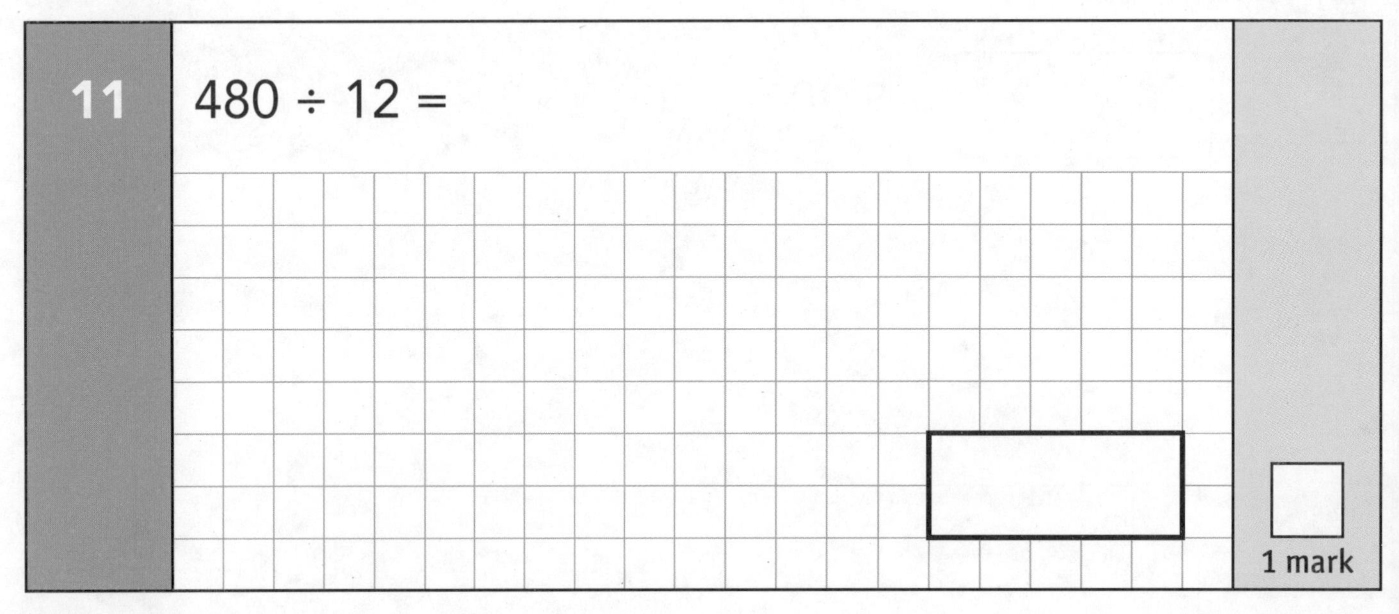

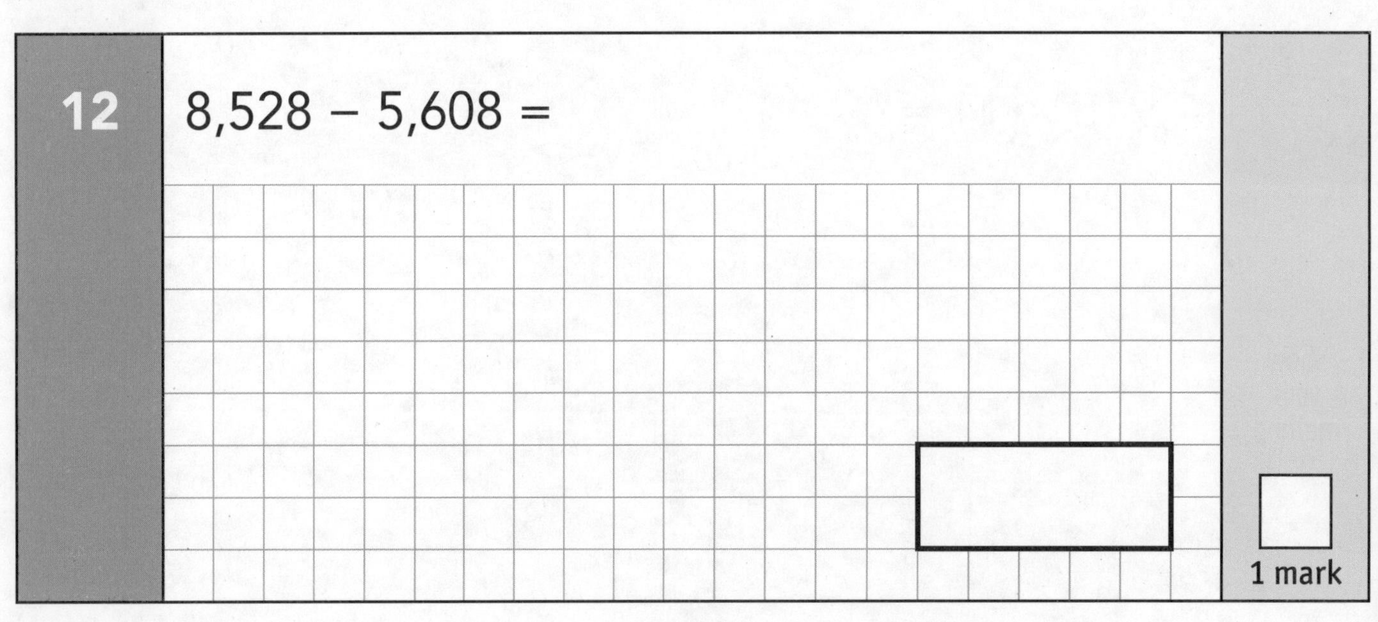

/4

Total for this page

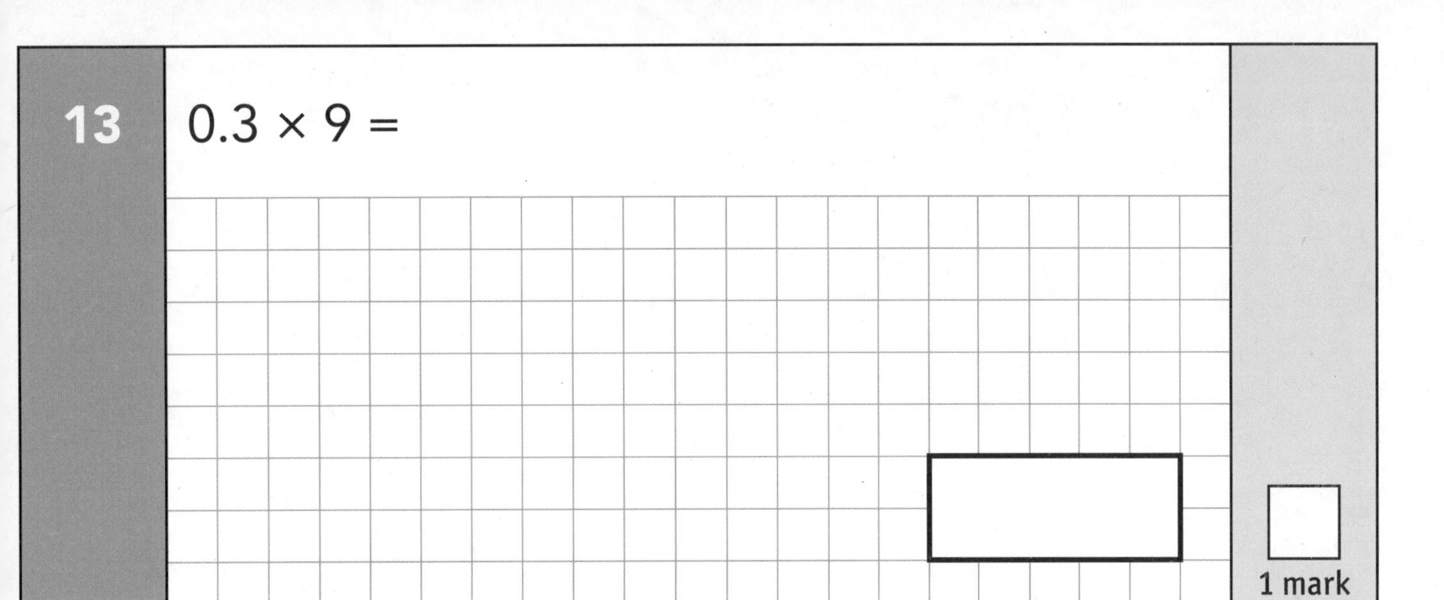

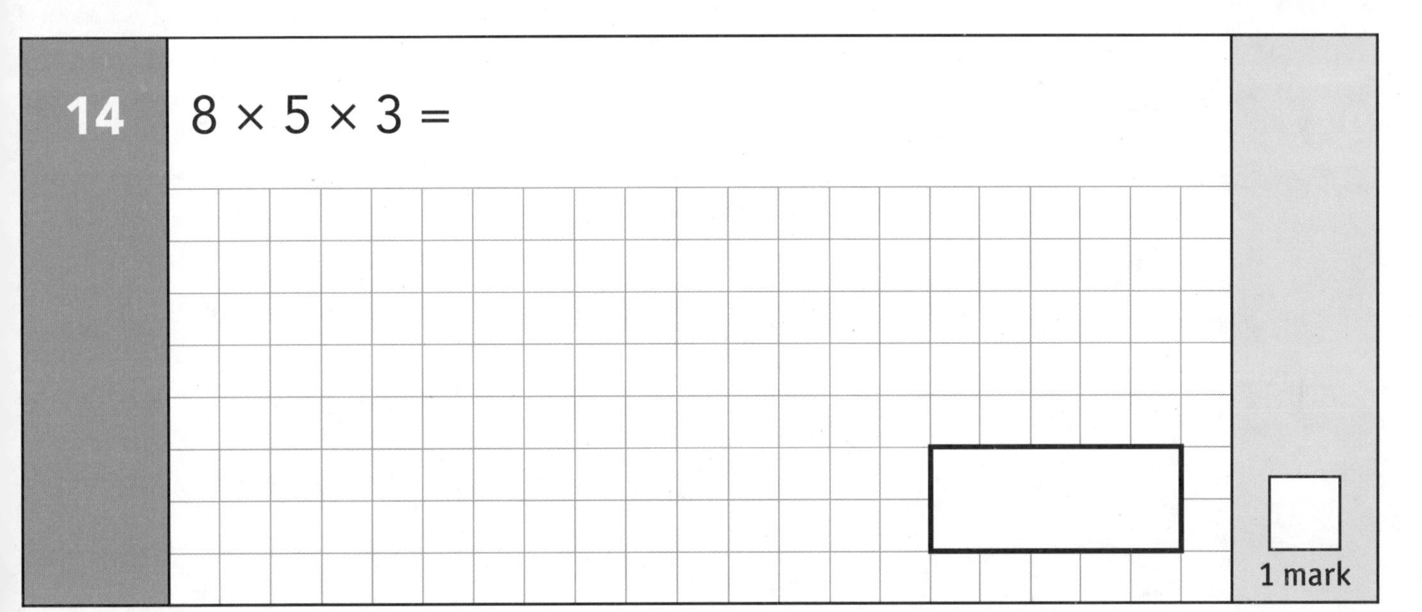

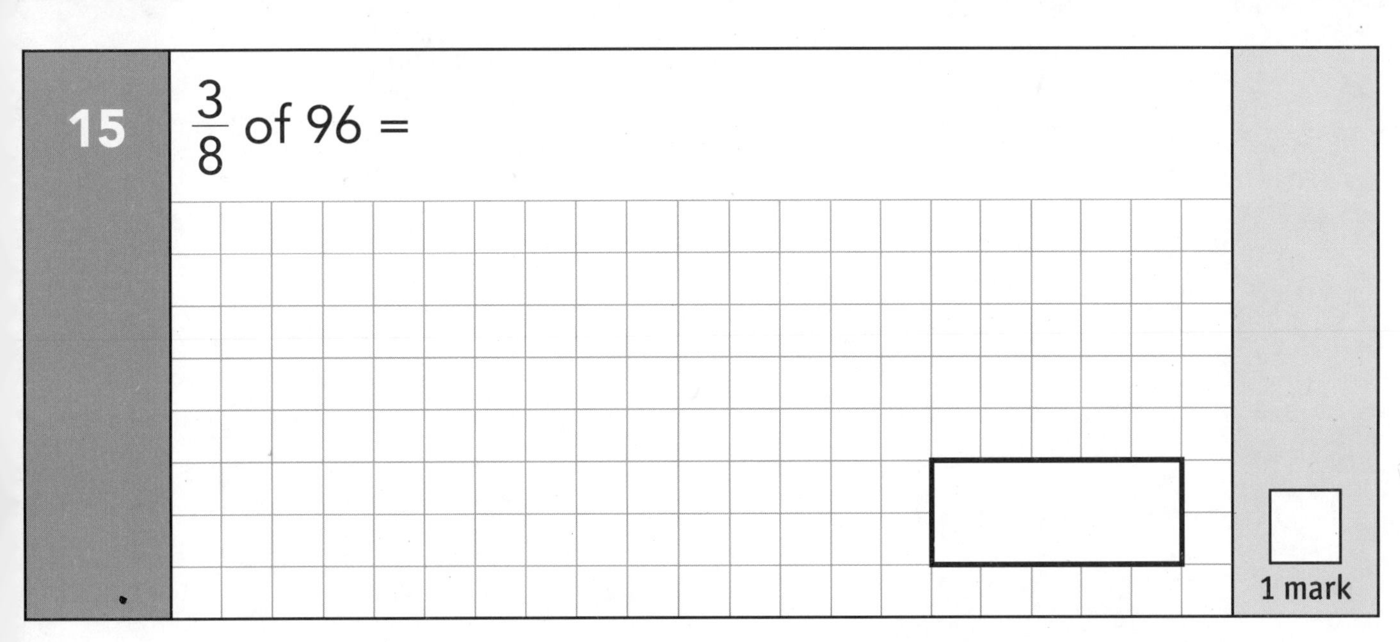

/3

Total for this page

16 $4.6 + 0.08 =$

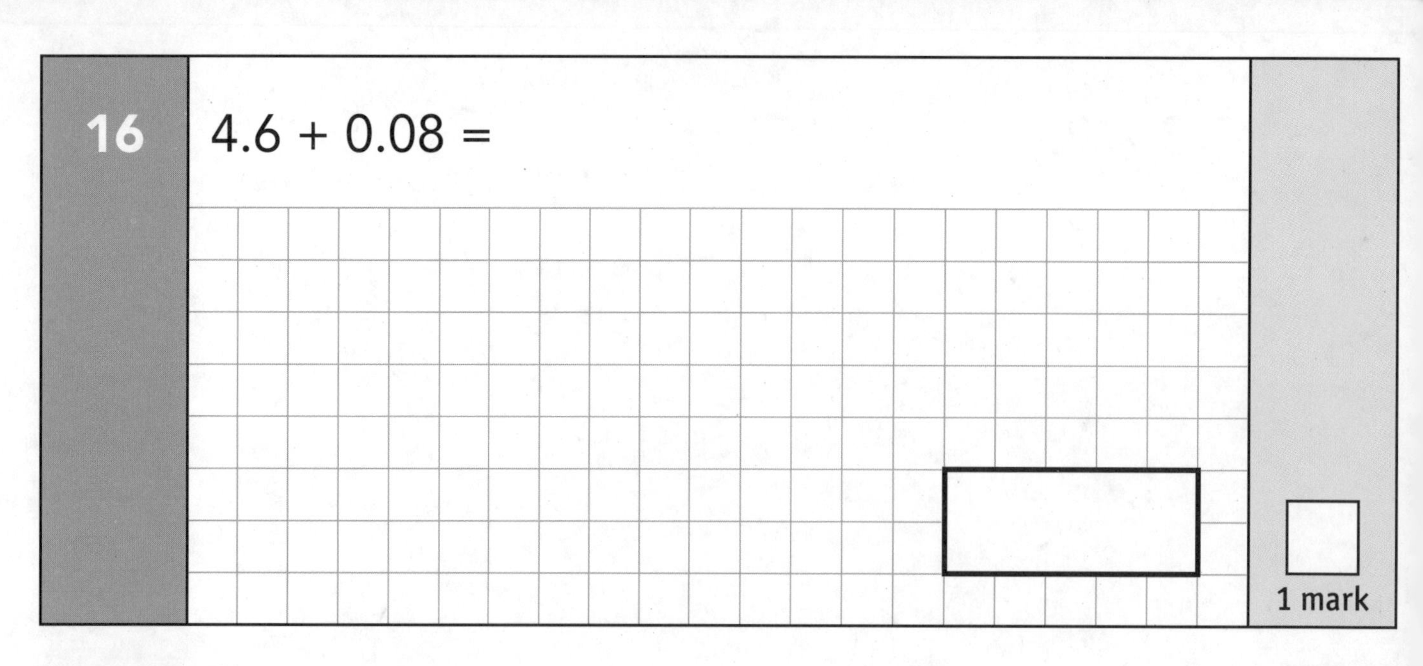

1 mark

17 30% of $2,000 =$

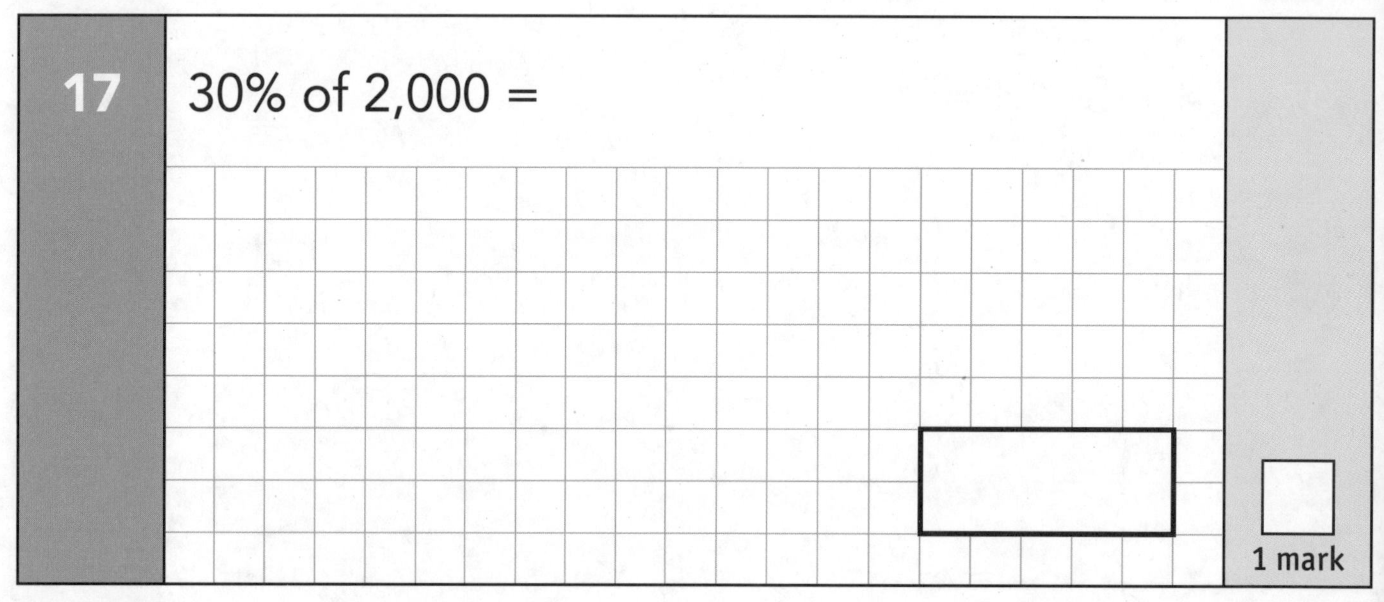

1 mark

18 $6,872 \div 8 =$

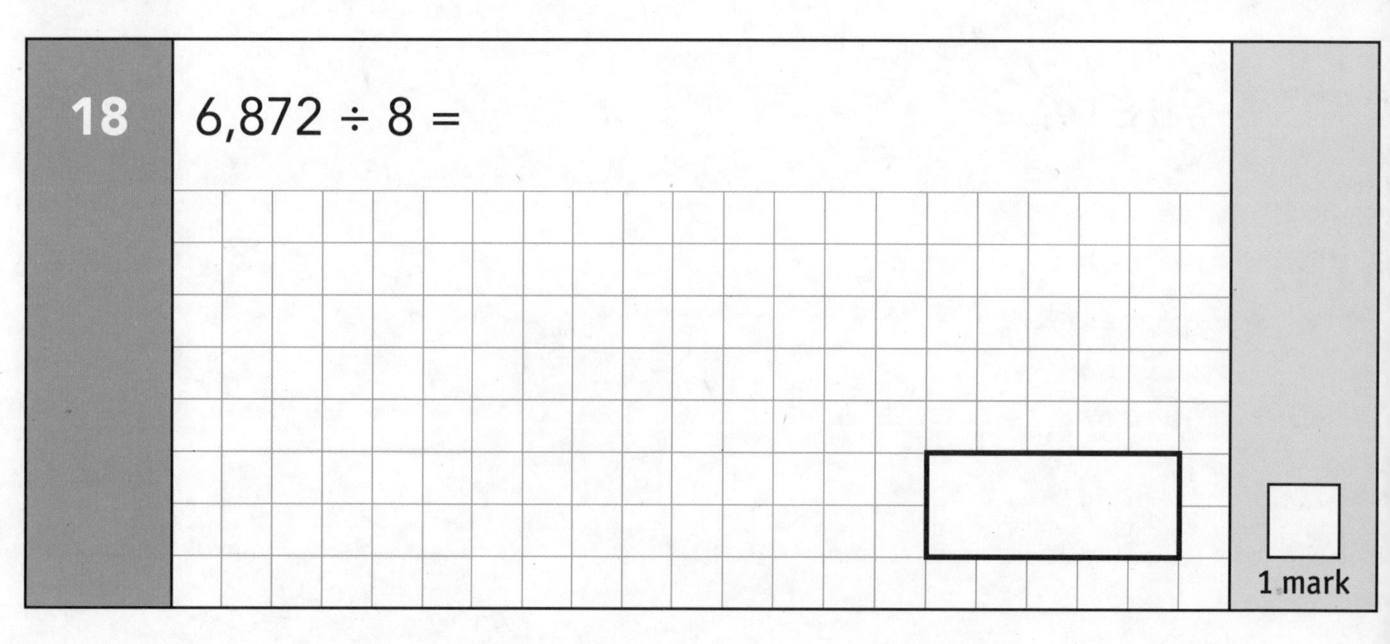

1 mark

/3

Total for this page

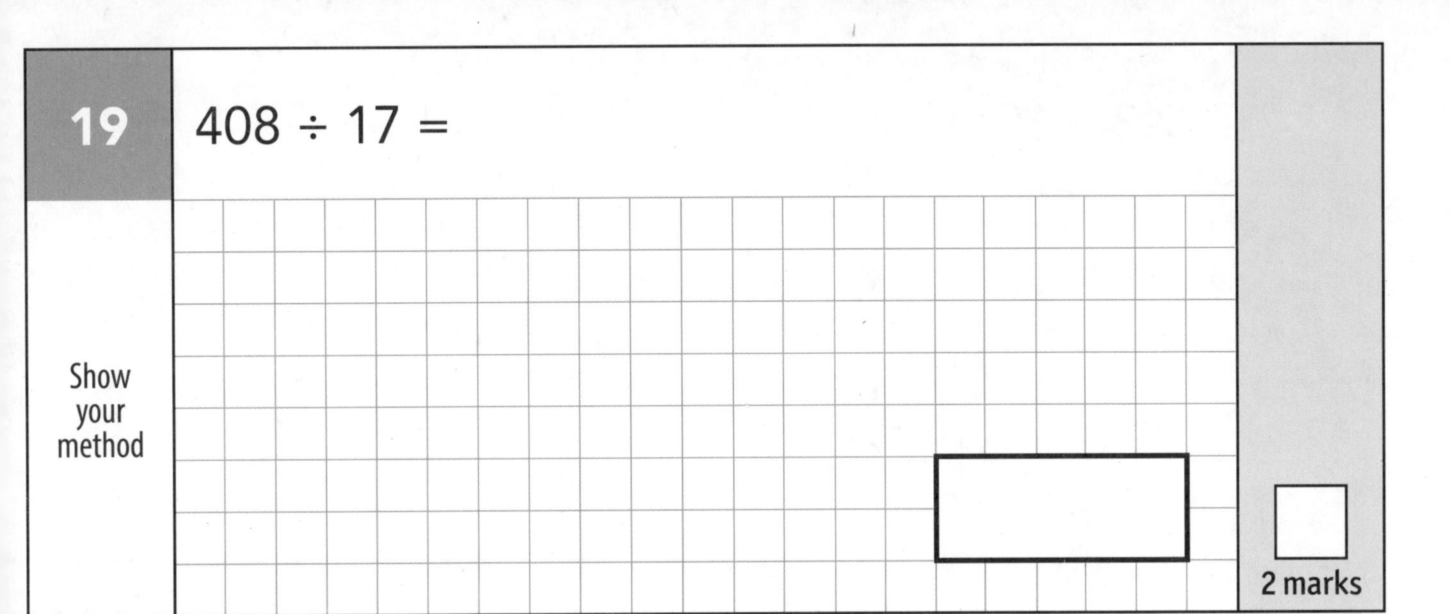

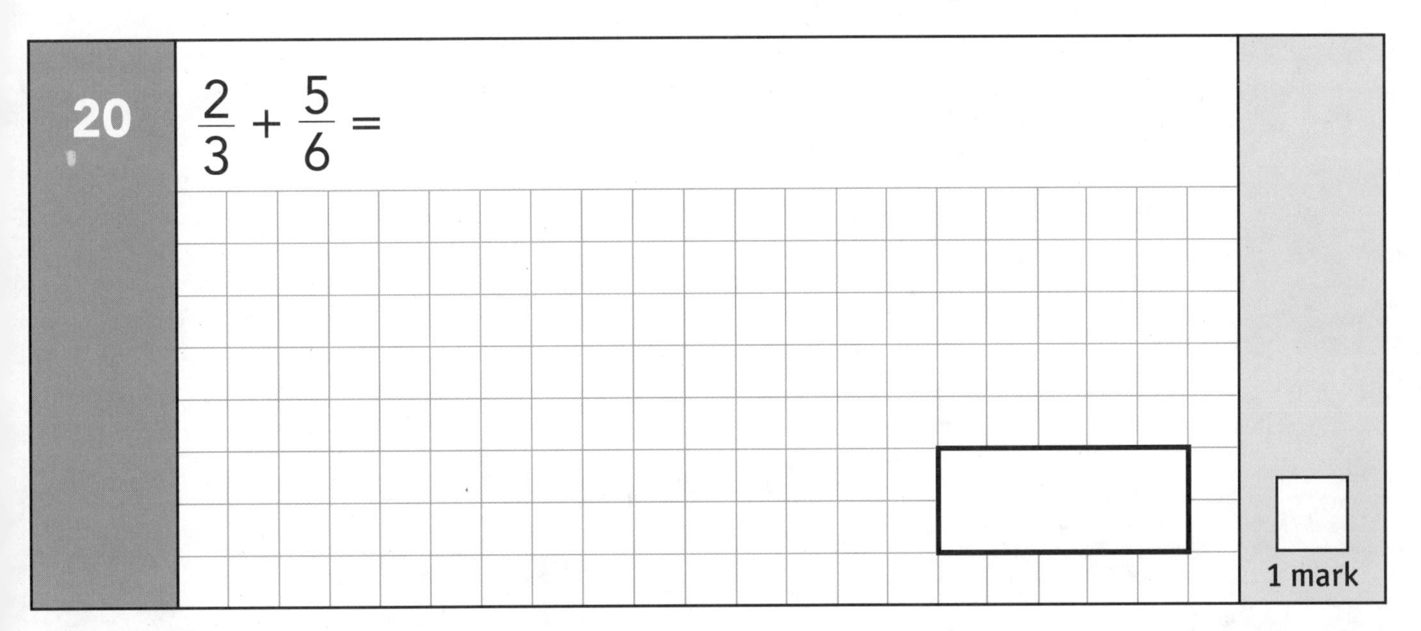

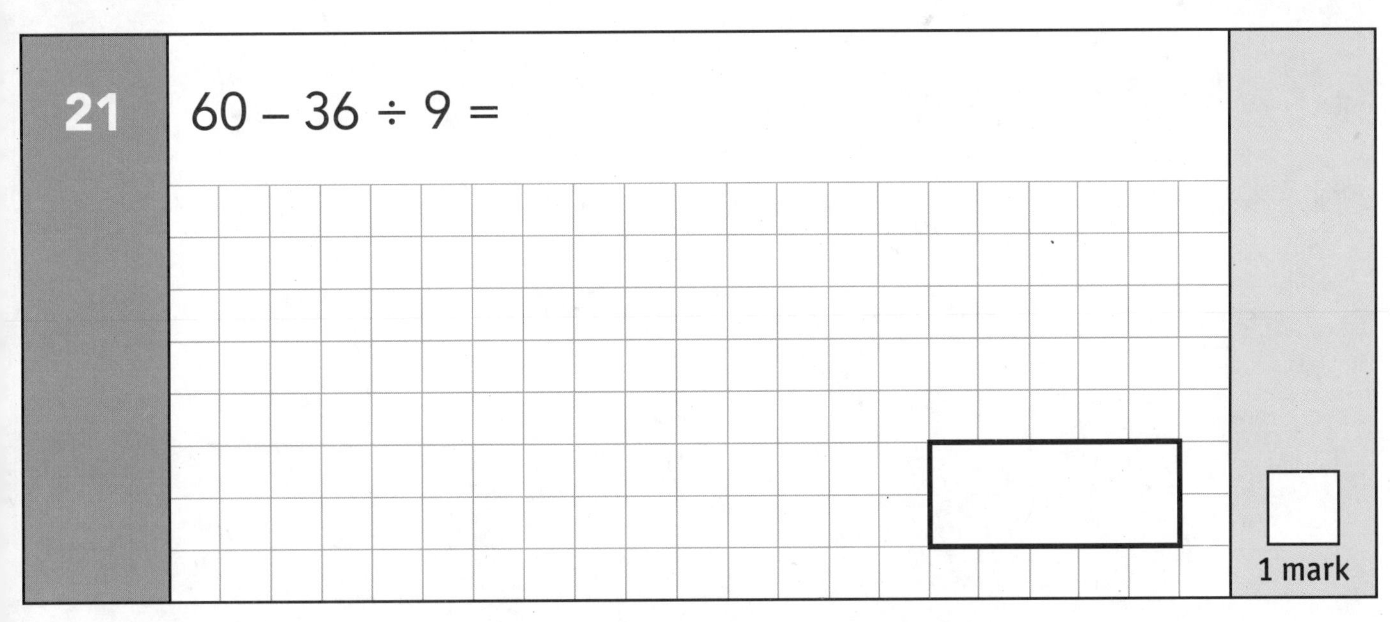

/4

Total for this page

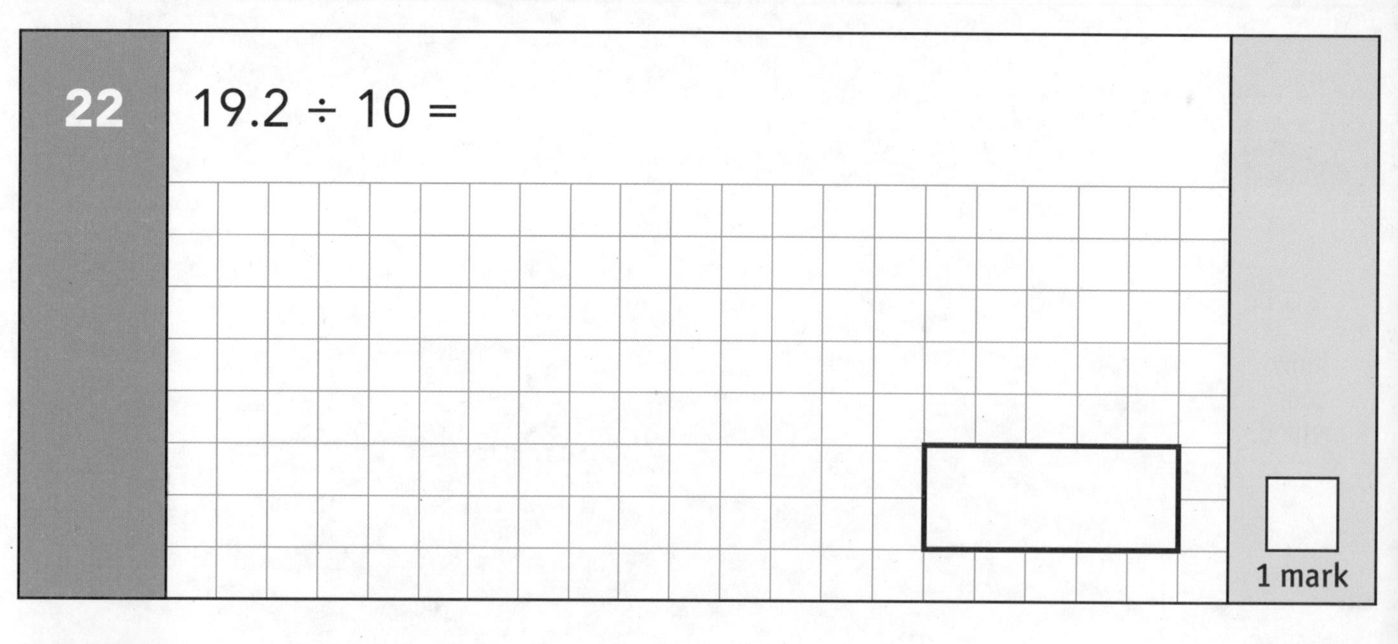

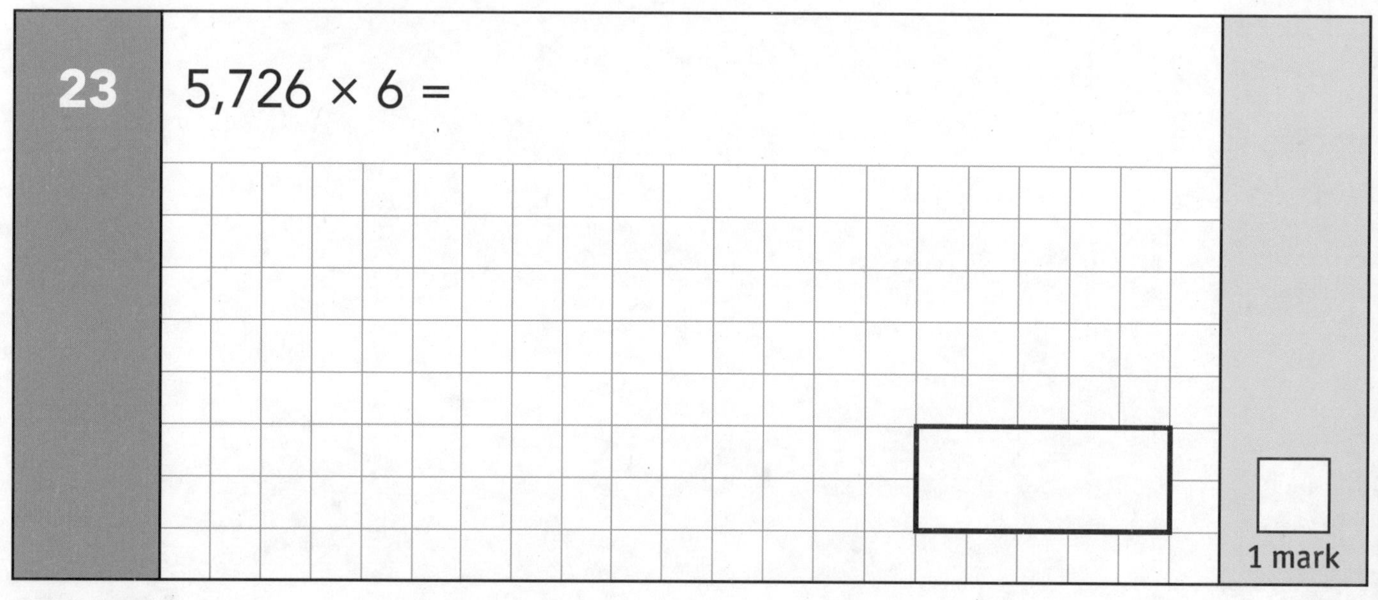

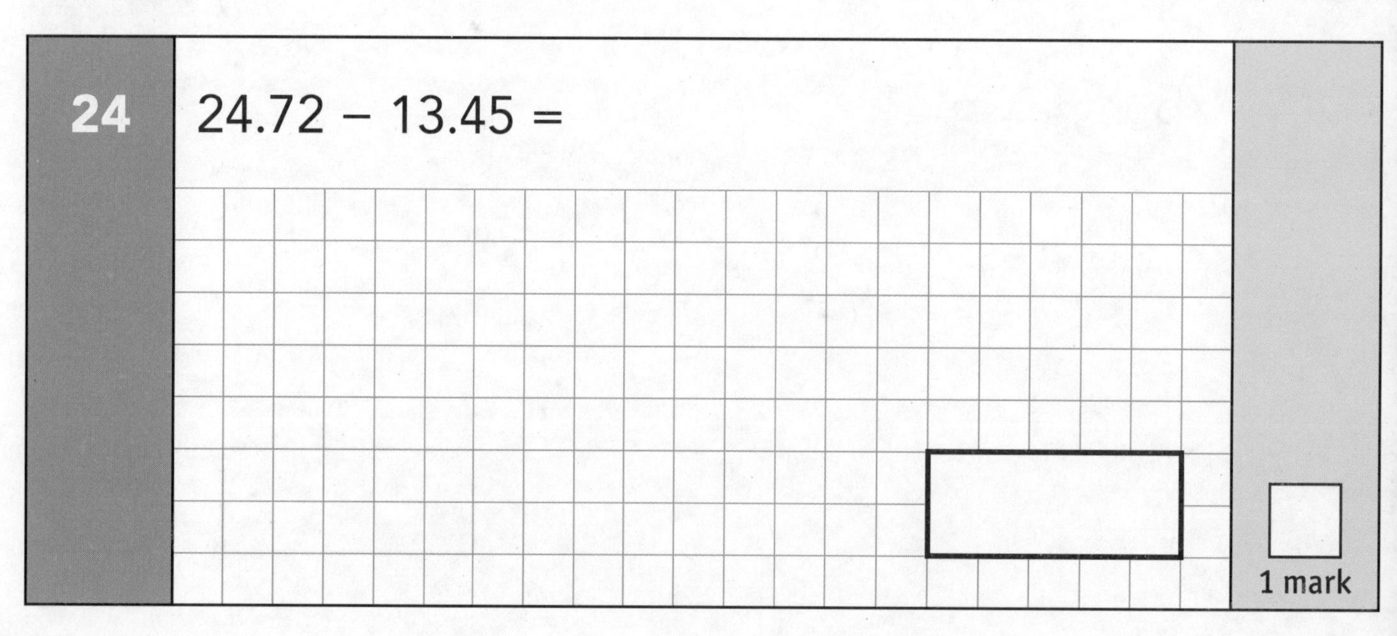

/3

Total for this page

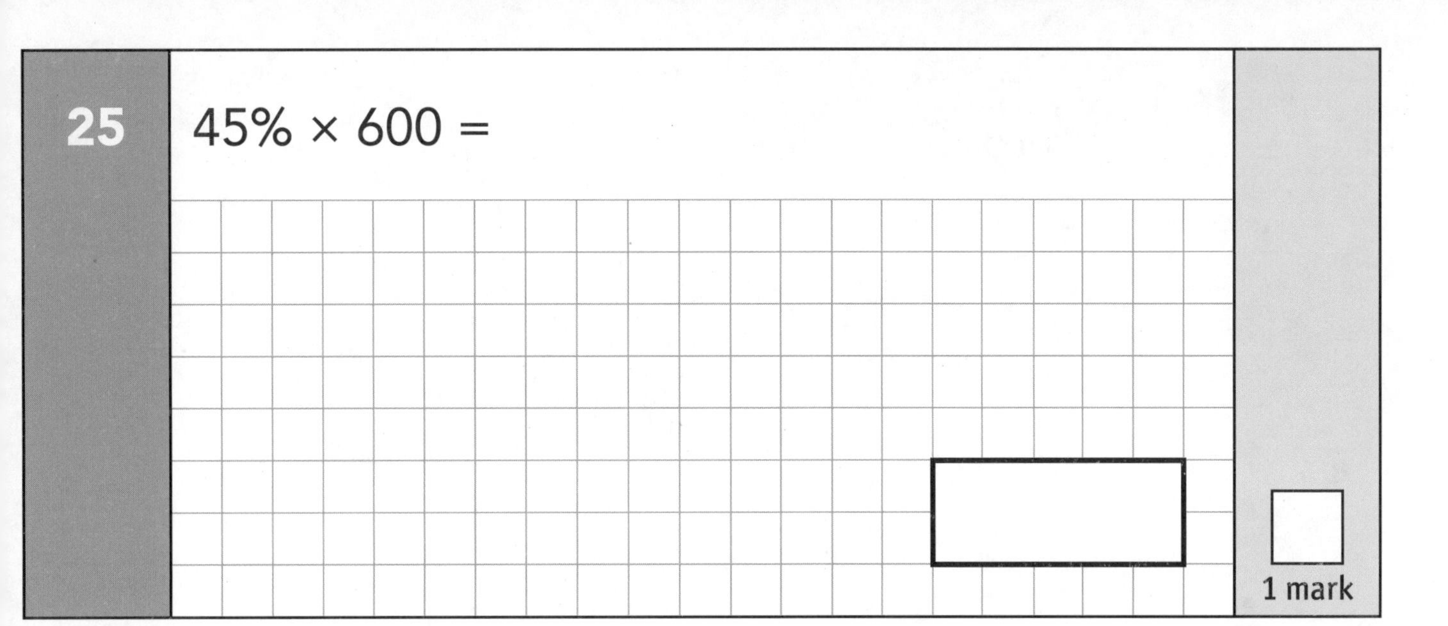

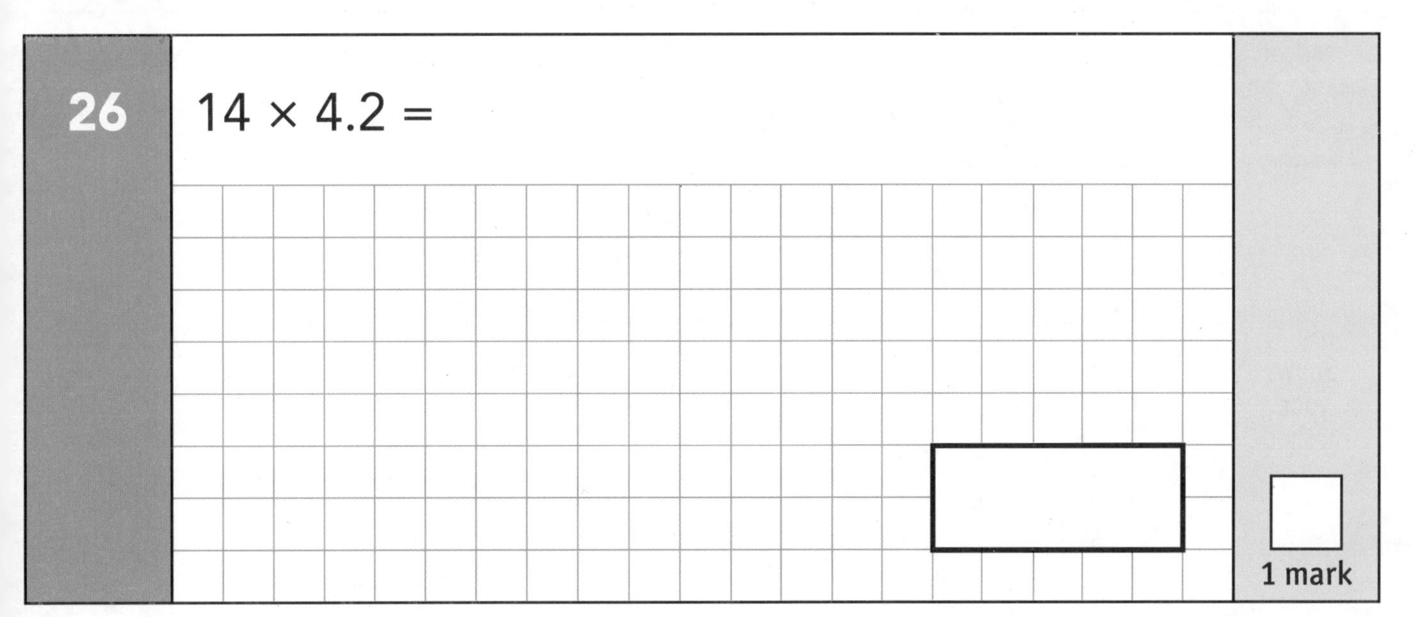

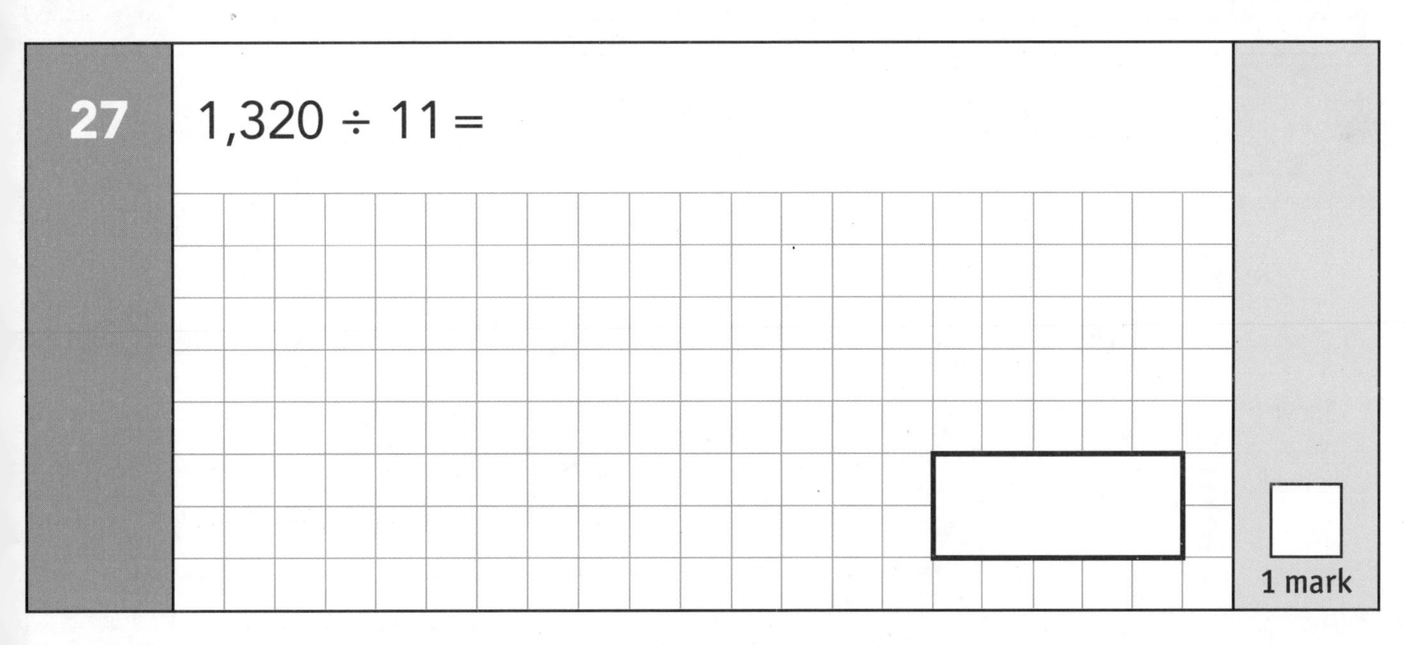

/3

Total for this page

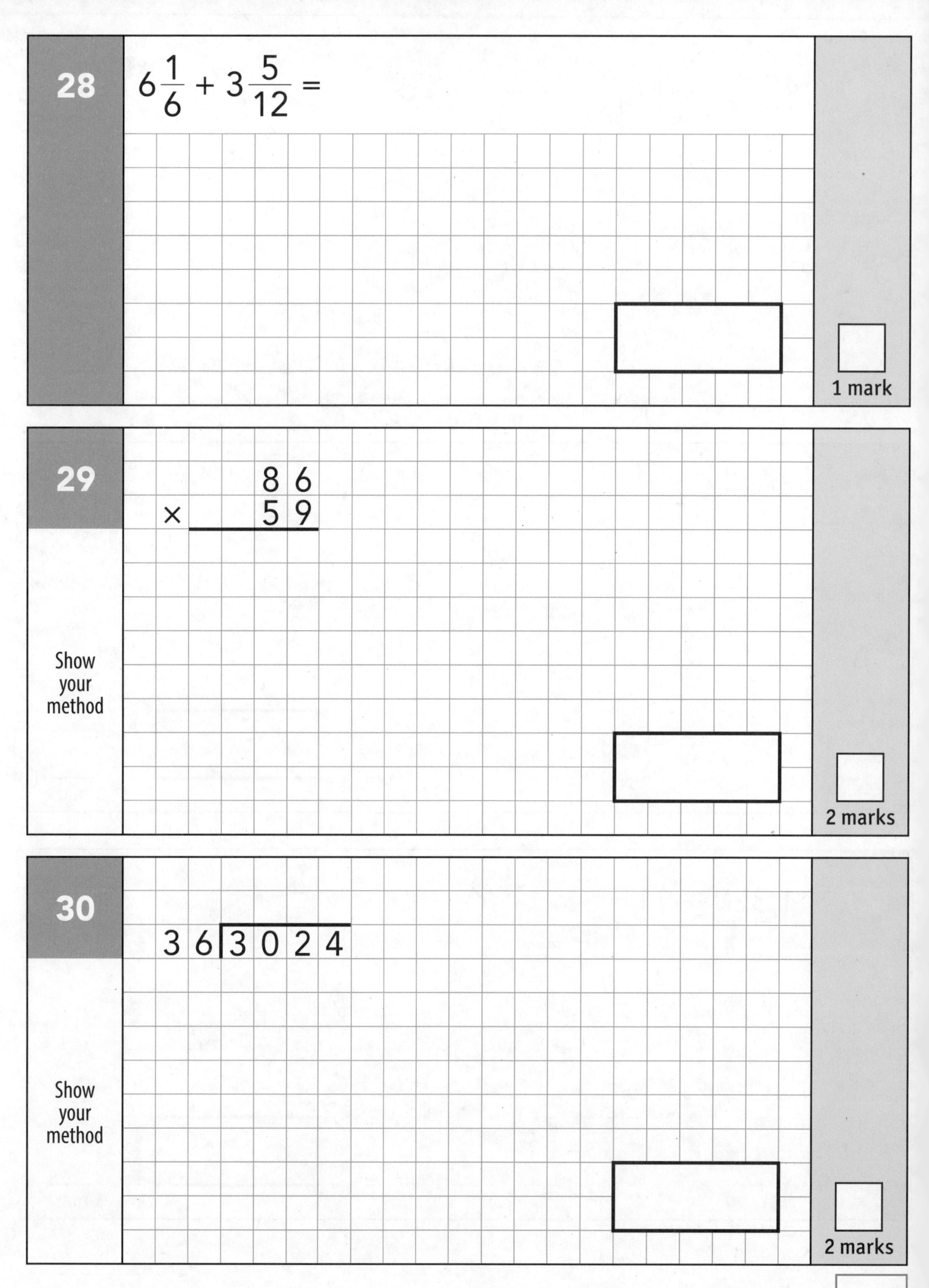

28

$6\frac{1}{6} + 3\frac{5}{12} =$

1 mark

29

$$\begin{array}{r} 86 \\ \times\ 59 \\ \hline \end{array}$$

Show your method

2 marks

30

$36\overline{)3024}$

Show your method

2 marks

/4

Total for this page

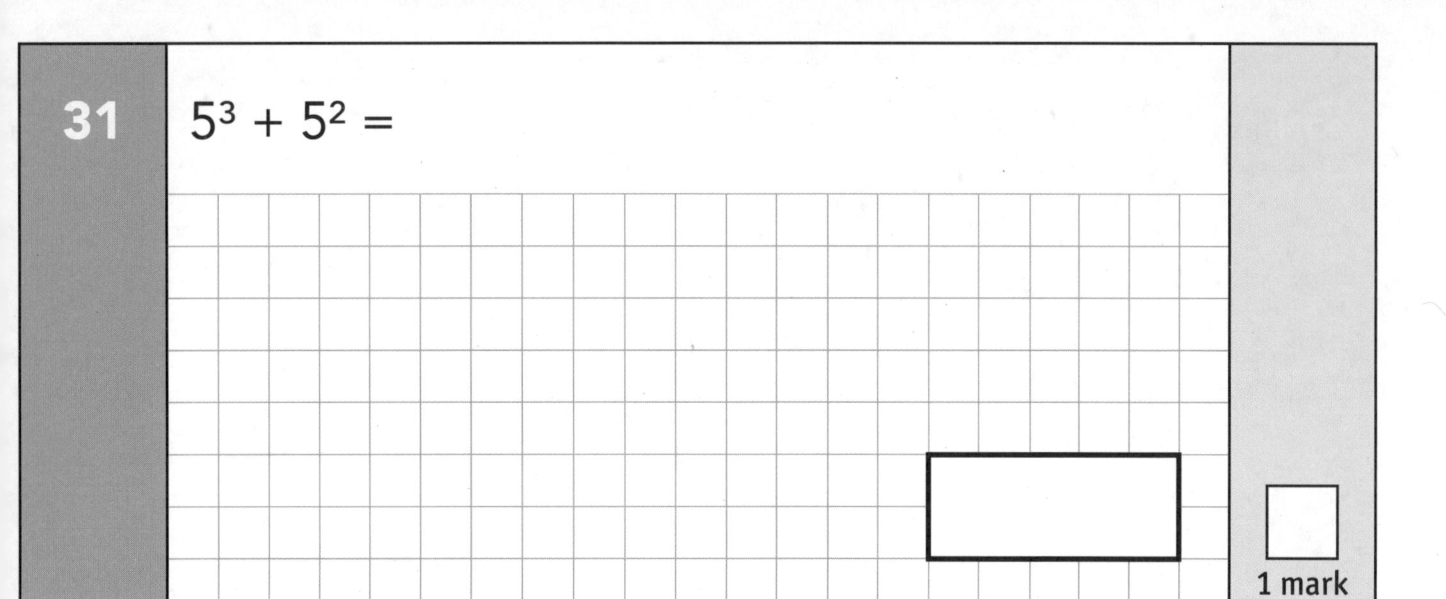

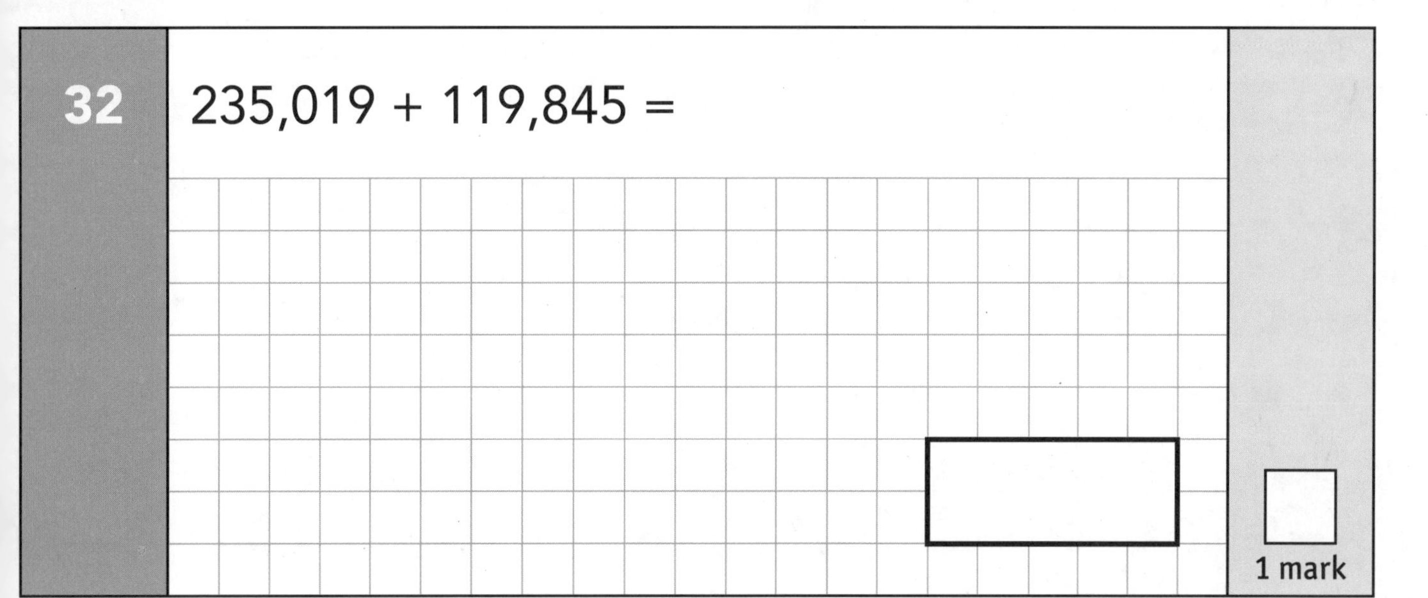

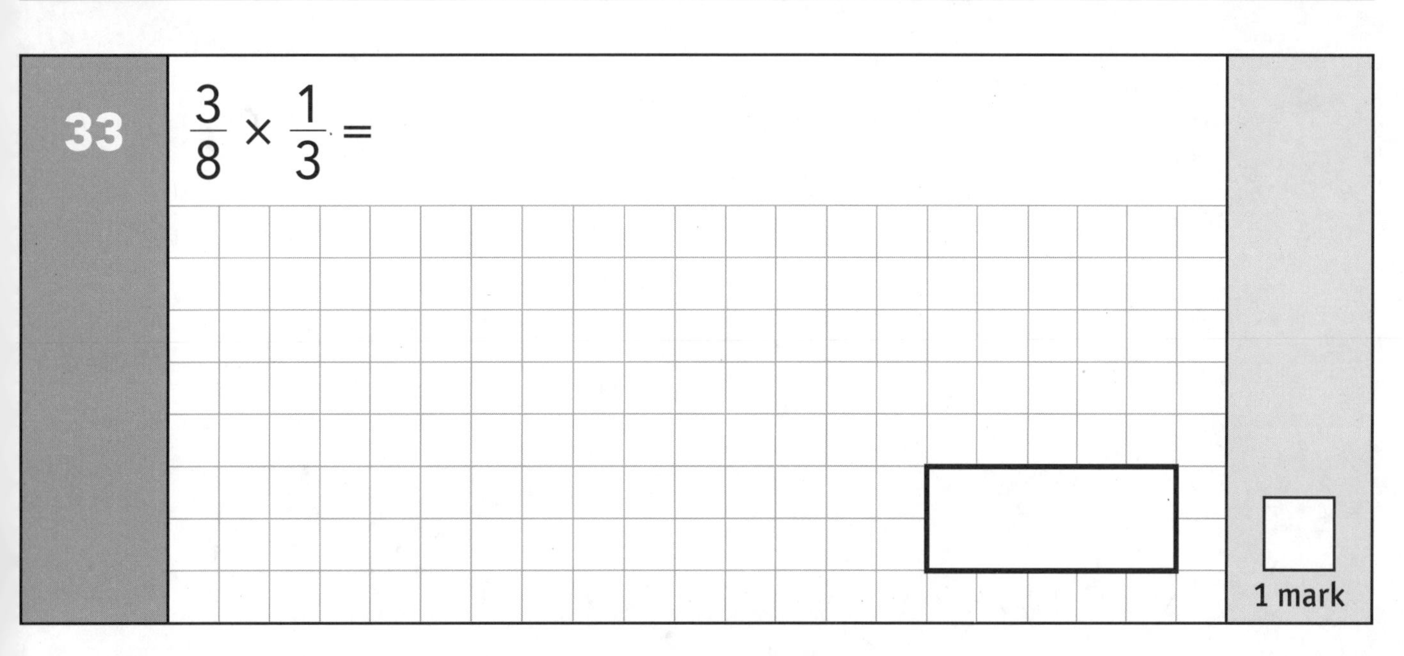

/4

Total for this page

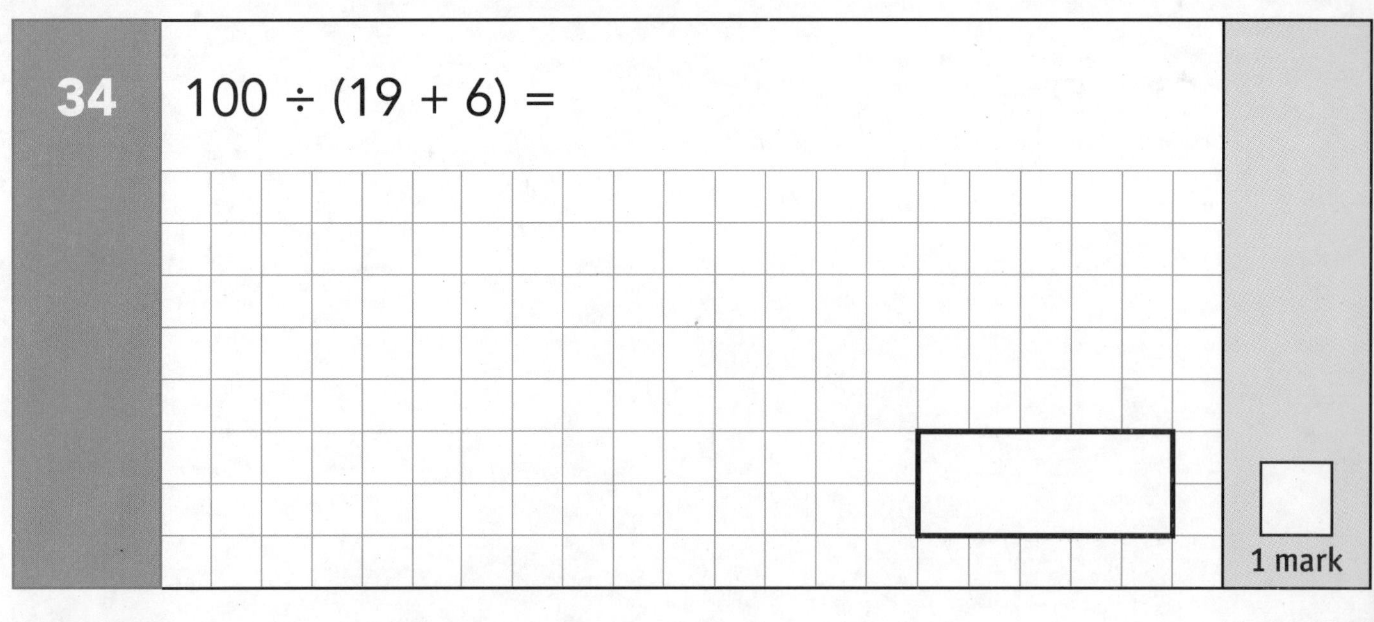

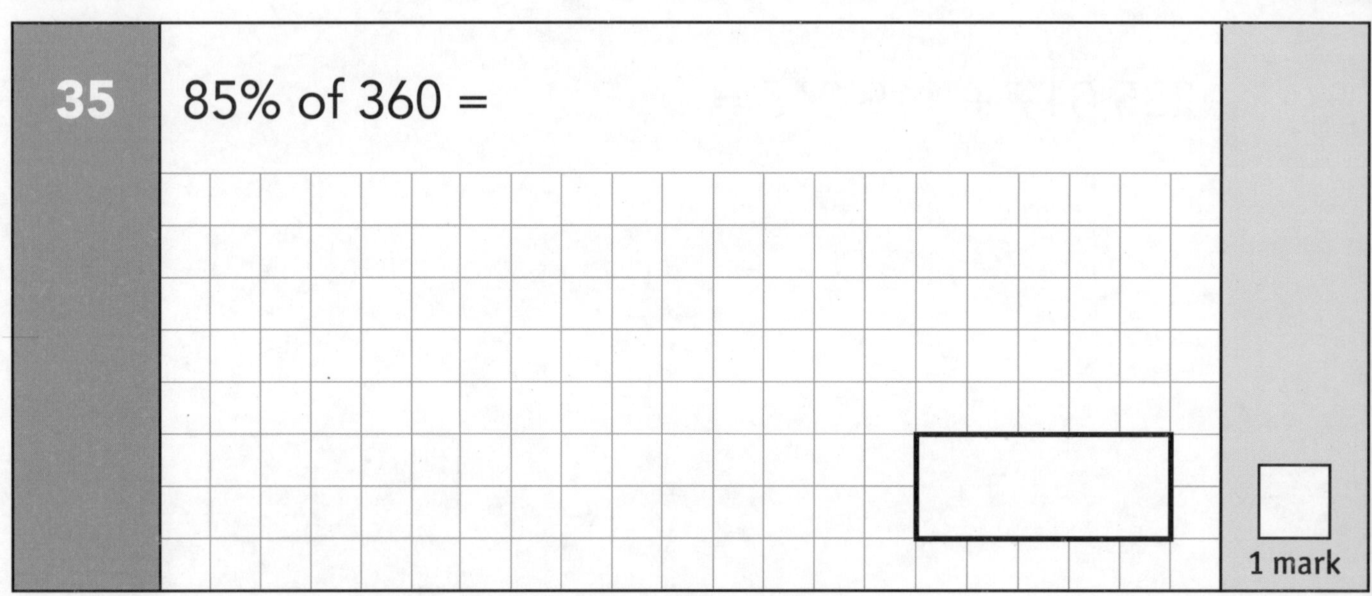

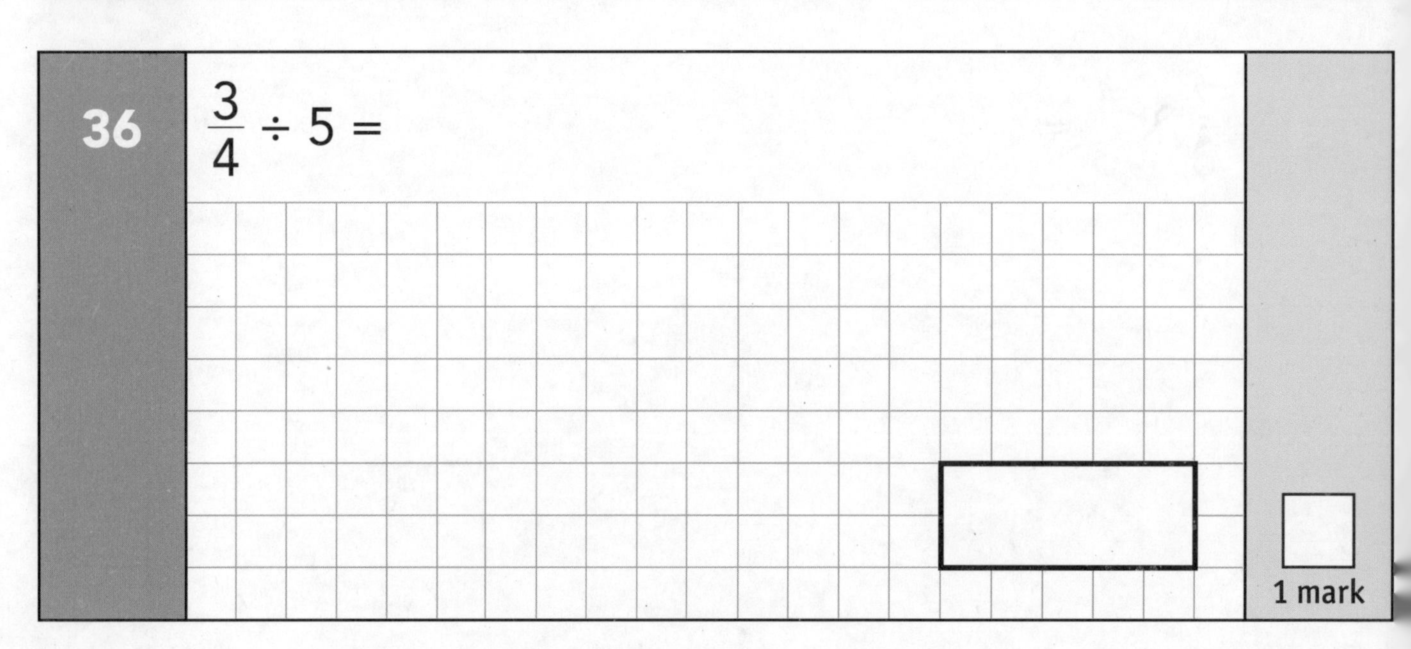

/3

Total for this page

Name:	Class:	Date:	Total marks: /35

Test 2, Paper 2: Reasoning

1 Draw lines to match calculations that have the same answers. One has been done for you.

132 ÷ 12	6 × 6
7 × 8	72 ÷ 9
9 × 4	44 ÷ 4
48 ÷ 6	112 ÷ 2

1 mark

2 Tick the shapes with **reflective symmetry**.

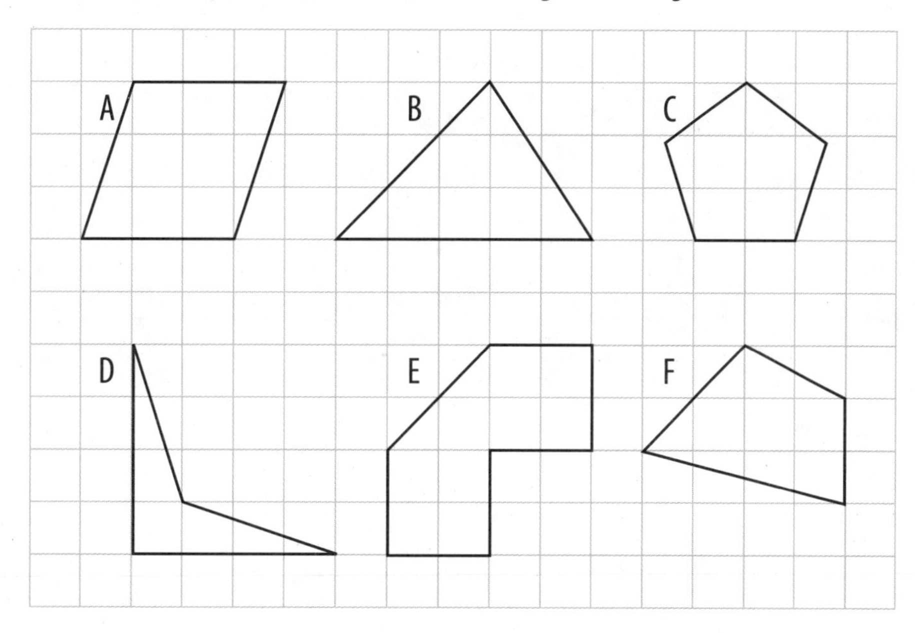

1 mark

/2

Total for this page

3 A pack of paper has 250 sheets.

7 children each take 8 sheets.

How many sheets of paper are left in the packet?

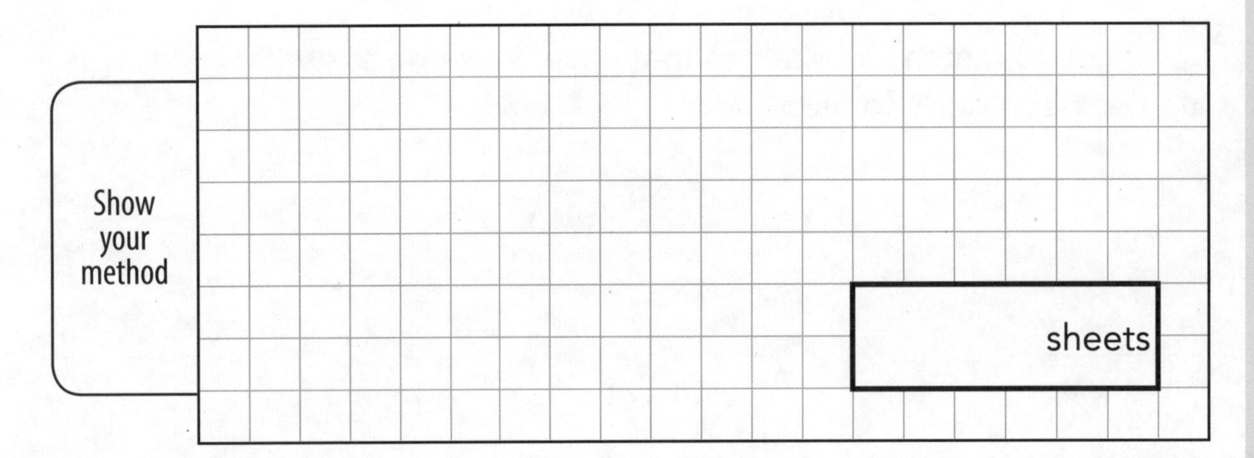

2 marks

4 Which of these is **not** equivalent to $\frac{3}{4}$?

Circle your answer.

0.75 $\frac{9}{12}$ 75% $\frac{75}{100}$ $\frac{14}{20}$

1 mark

5 What number is halfway between 0.8 and 2?

1 mark

/4

Total for this page

6 Remi thinks of a whole number.

He squares it and then adds 50

His new number is **less than** 100

What is the **largest** starting number that Remi could have?

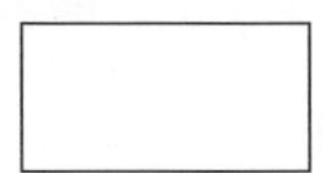

1 mark

7 Jayden pours 700 ml of water into the jug.

a) Draw a line to show the level of the water in the jug.

b) How much **more** water is needed to fill the jug? litres

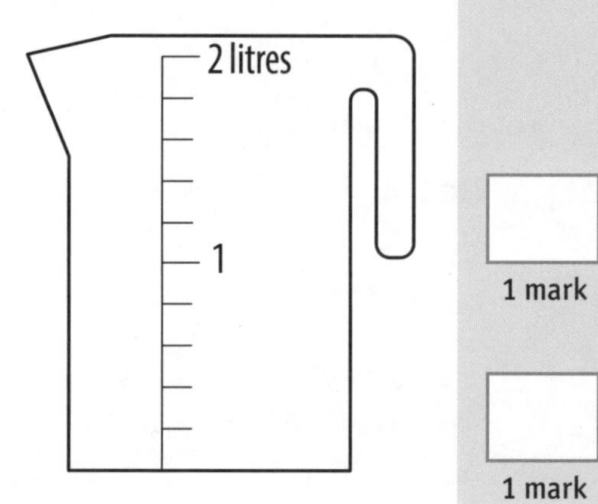

1 mark

1 mark

8 Sara had some money.

She spent 40p on a drink.

She spent £1.60 on a sandwich.

She has spent **one-third** of her money.

How much money did Sara have to **start with**?

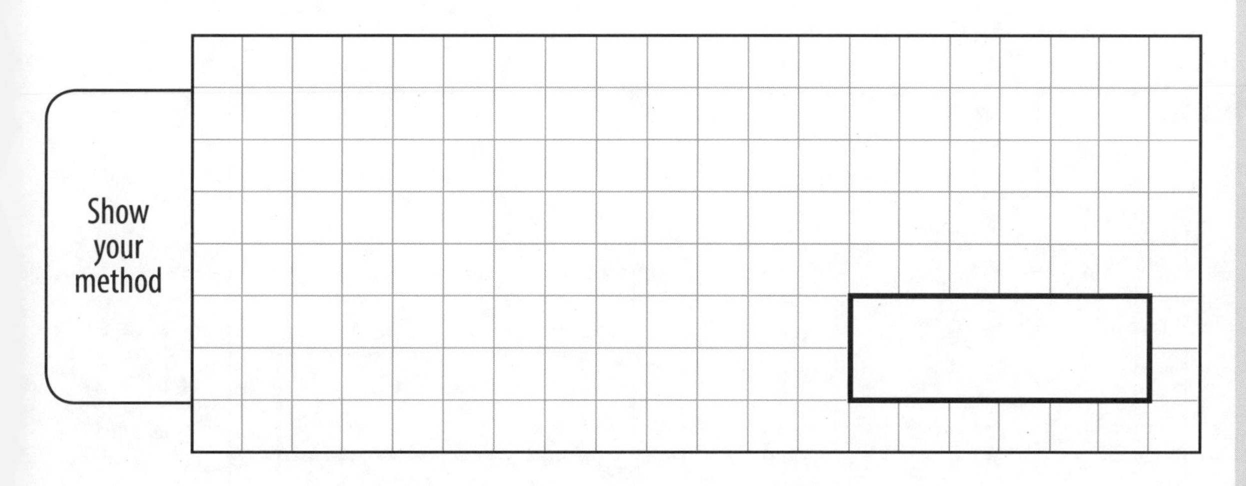

2 marks

/5

Total for this page

9 a)

Jacob ran a race in three and a half minutes.

Renuka took 20 seconds longer.

How many **seconds** did Renuka take to run the race?

[ ] seconds

1 mark

b)

Ryan made a jump of four and a half metres.

Lindsey's jump was 30 cm longer.

How long was Lindsey's jump? [ ] cm

1 mark

10 A recipe for milkshake uses 150 ml of milk for every 50 g of fruit.

How many grams of fruit should be used for 750 ml of milk?

Show your method

[ ] g

2 marks

/4

Total for this page

11 The pictogram shows the approximate costs of heating a small hotel at the start of a year.

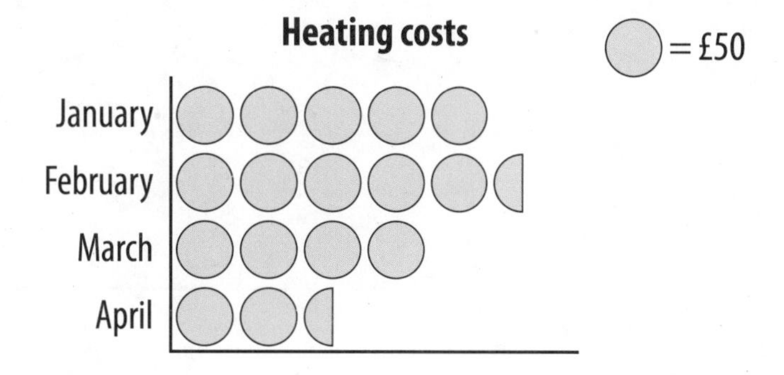

a) How much more was spent on heating in January than in April? ☐

1 mark

b) The total amount spent in **two** months was **£400**

Which two months?

__________ and __________

1 mark

12 Complete these statements using **different two-digit** numbers each time.

a) 6 and 4 are a factor pair of ☐

b) 6 and 4 are also factors of ☐ and ☐

c) 6 and 4 are factors of the square number ☐

2 marks

13 Here is part of a number line.

Write the missing numbers in the boxes.

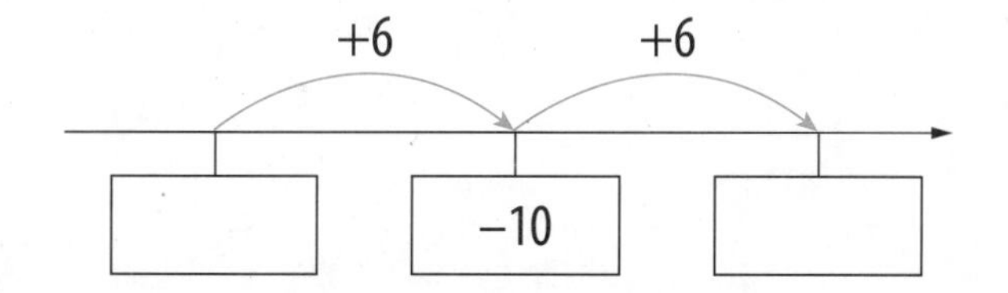

2 marks

Total for this page

14 Tick the calculations that could be used to find the total shaded fraction.

A $\frac{1}{2} + \frac{1}{8}$ ☐

B $\frac{1}{3} + \frac{1}{4}$ ☐

C $\frac{1}{4} + \frac{1}{4} + \frac{1}{8}$ ☐

D $\frac{3}{8} + \frac{1}{2}$ ☐

E $\frac{1}{4} + \frac{3}{8}$ ☐

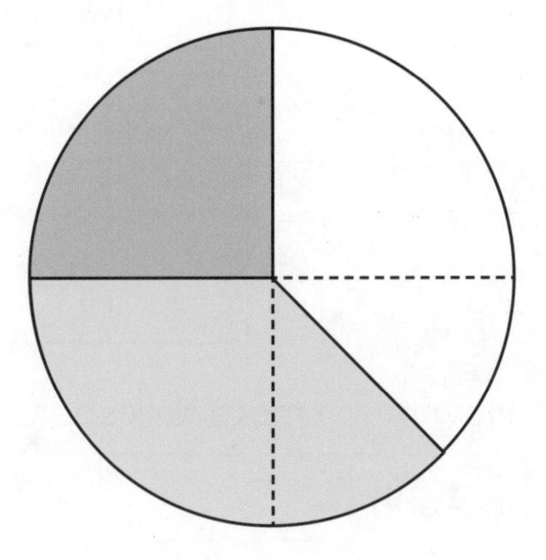

1 mark

15 a) Write the number that is **five less** than **five million**.

b) Write the number that is **one hundred thousand less** than **five million**.

2 marks

16 Calculate the **perimeter** of this shape.

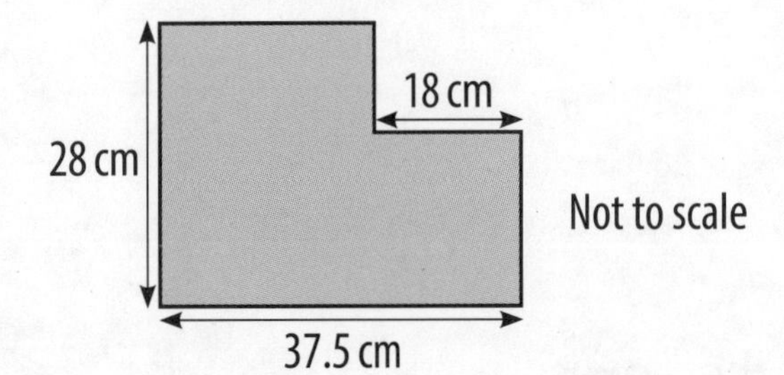

cm

1 mark

/4

Total for this page

17 Tick the net that is used to make this cuboid.

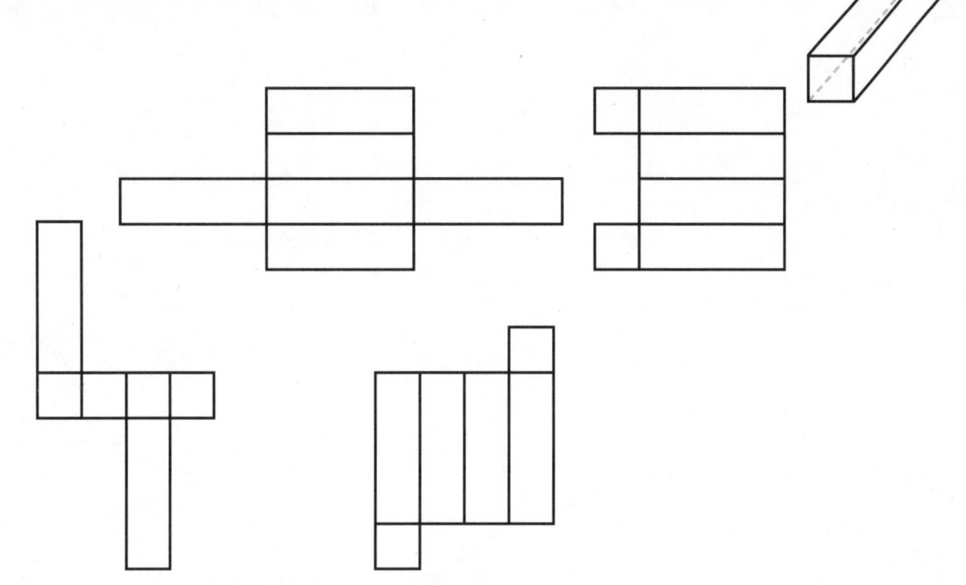

1 mark

18 The table below shows the height of six trees.

Trees	Height (cm)
Tree 1	267
Tree 2	437
Tree 3	312
Tree 4	265
Tree 5	259
Tree 6	266

What is the mean height of the trees?

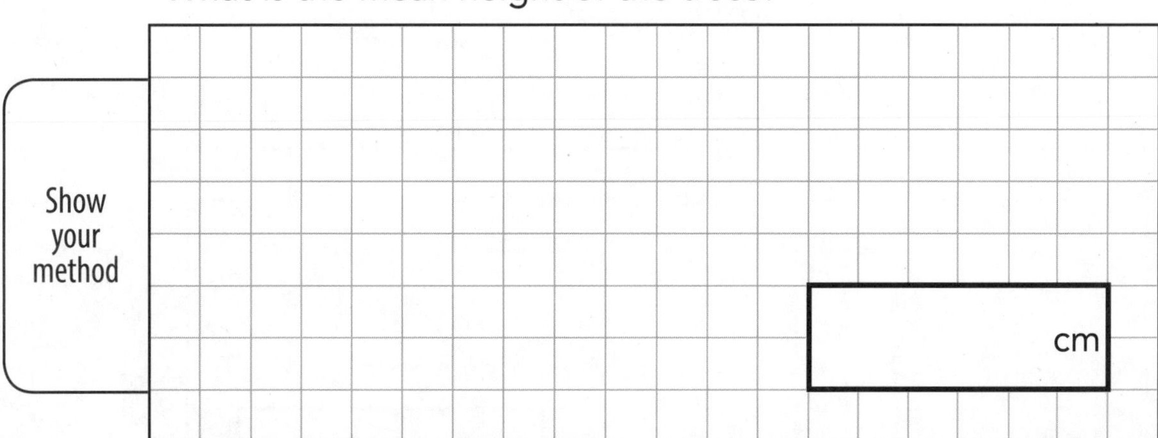

2 marks

/3

Total for this page

19 A triangle is translated from position **A** to position **B**.

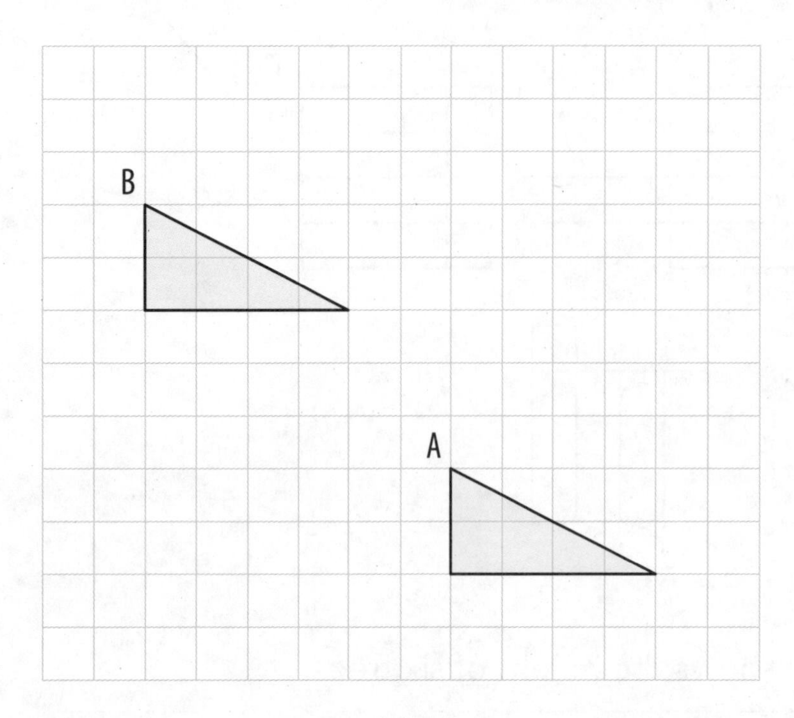

Complete the sentence.

The triangle has moved ☐ squares to the left

and ☐ squares up.

1 mark

20 What is the **area** of this shape?

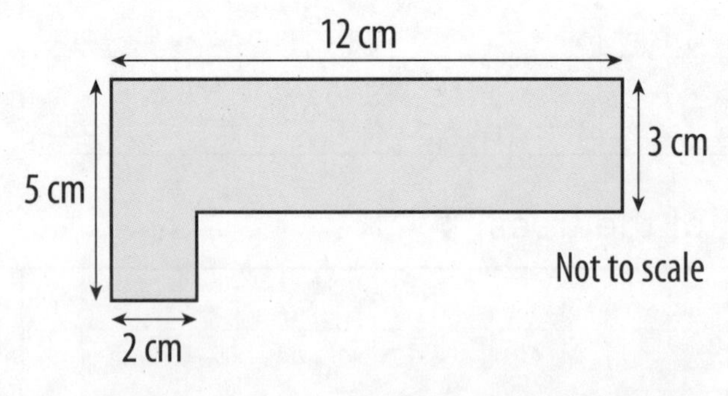

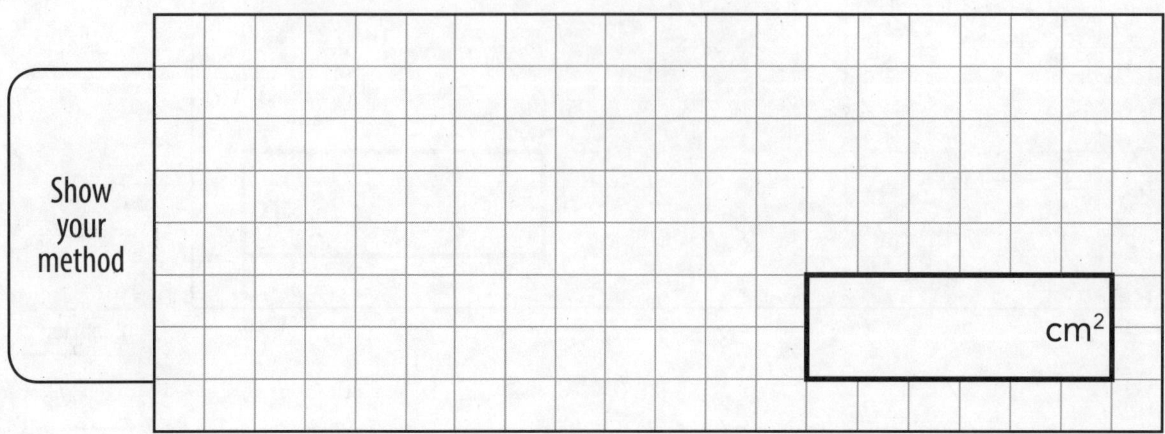

2 marks

/3

Total for this page

21 Write these fractions in order starting with the **smallest**.

$1\frac{2}{3}$ $1\frac{4}{5}$ $\frac{18}{15}$

smallest **largest**

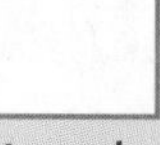

1 mark

22 $3m \div 2n = 6$

$n^3 = 125$

What are the values of ***m*** and ***n***?

$m =$ $n =$

Show your method

3 marks

/4

Total for this page

Name:	Class:	Date:	Total marks: /35

Test 2, Paper 3: Reasoning

1 Draw lines to match the number that has a digit with each value shown.

One has been done for you.

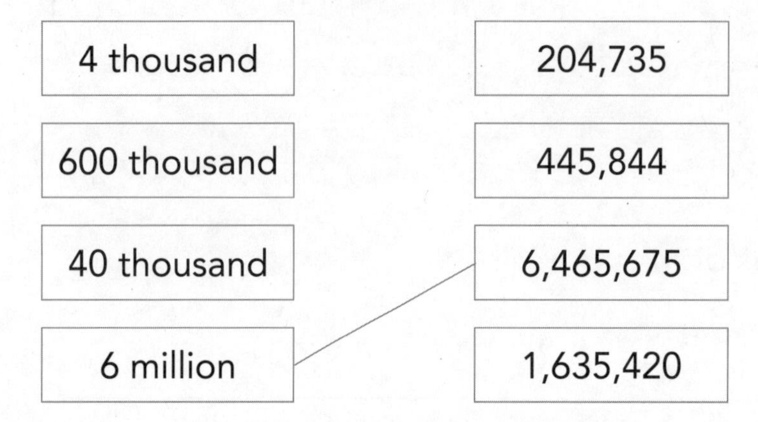

1 mark

2 Write the letter of the shape that has one pair of parallel sides **and** one pair of perpendicular sides.

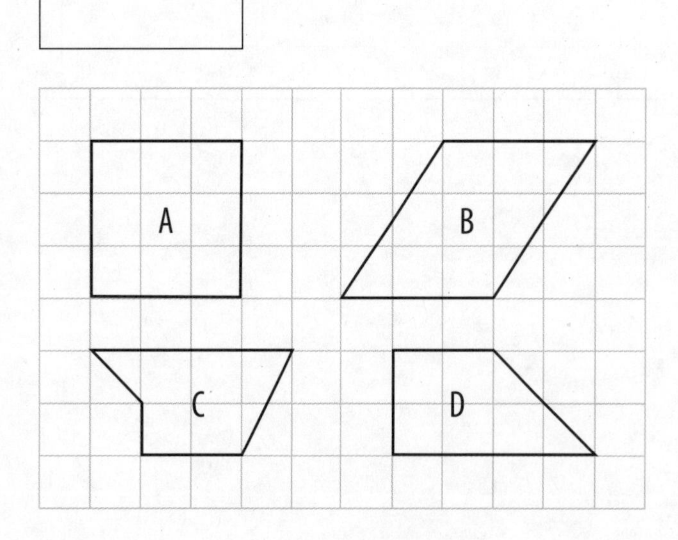

1 mark

/2

Total for this page

3 Ben and Eli are playing a computer game.

Their target score is 9,999 points.

They have scored 4,028 points on Level 1 and 3,986 points on Level 2.

How many points do they need to score on Level 3 to reach their target?

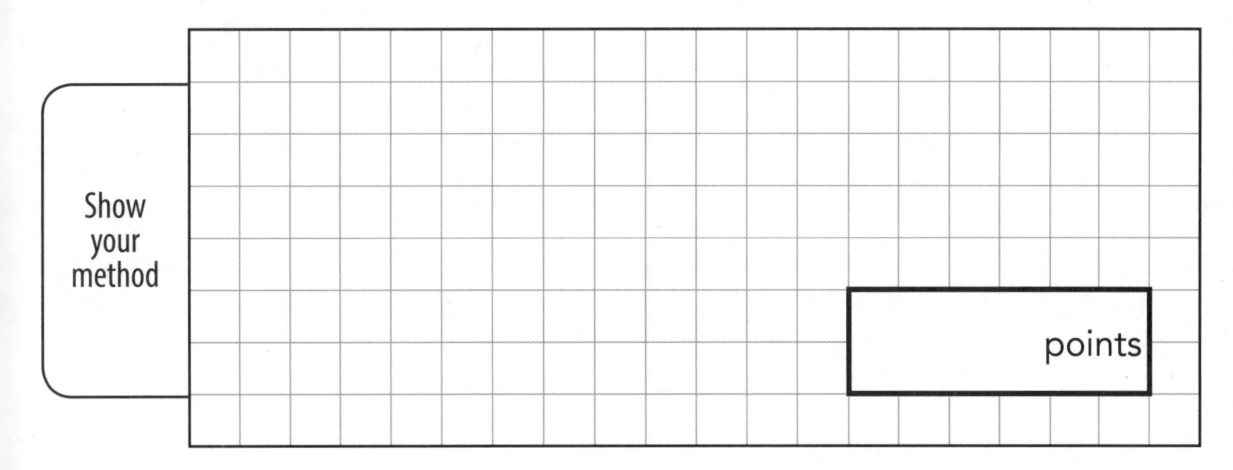

2 marks

4 Circle the numbers that are **greater than** 45,500

45,499 45,501 50,000 45,050

1 mark

5 This thermometer shows the temperature inside.

The temperature outside is 20°C **lower**.

Circle the temperature outside.

20°C 0°C –7°C 17°C –3°C

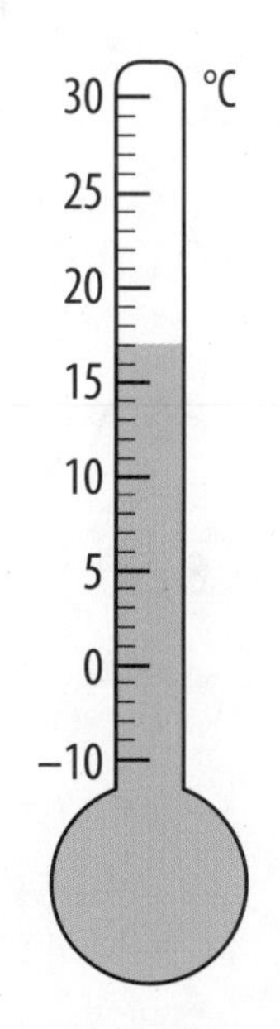

1 mark

/4

Total for this page

6 On Sunday, Farmer Mo picked 1,305 red apples and 978 green apples.

On Monday, he picked 600 red apples and 1,235 green apples.

How many more green apples did he pick?

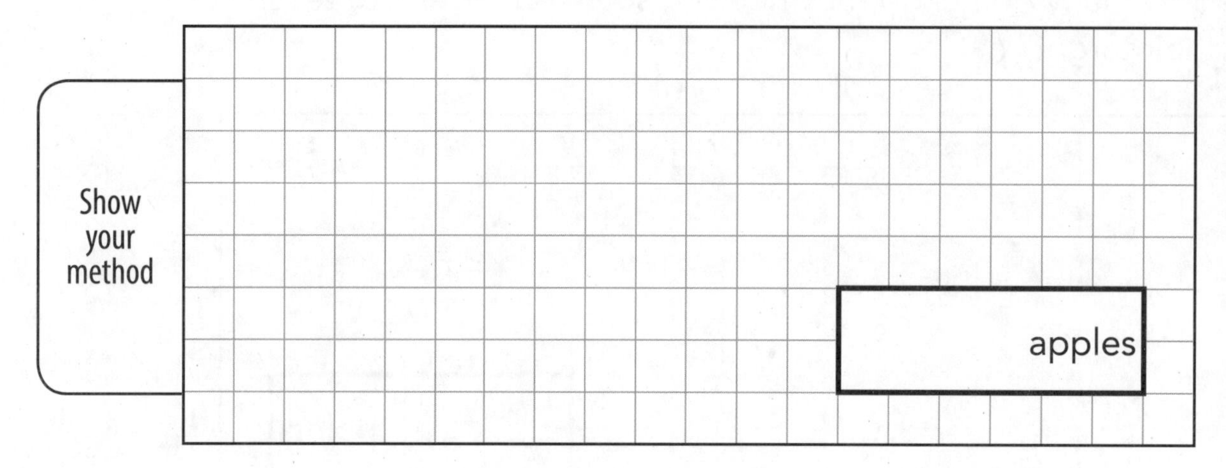

2 marks

7 Here are six cards.

÷ 10	÷ 100	÷ 1000
× 10	× 100	× 1000

Use a card to complete each calculation.

8.5 [ ] = 0.085

8.5 [ ] = 85

8.5 [ ] = 8,500

2 marks

/4

Total for this page

8 Here are some fraction cards.

Choose the correct fraction cards to complete the calculations.

$\frac{3}{10}$	$\frac{3}{5}$	$\frac{1}{2}$	$\frac{7}{5}$	$\frac{7}{10}$	$\frac{2}{3}$

a) $\square + \square = 1\frac{1}{5}$

1 mark

b) $\square - \square = 1\frac{1}{10}$

1 mark

9 A library has 120 books. $\frac{2}{5}$ of the books are non-fiction.

How many books are non-fiction? $\square$

1 mark

10 These two shapes are made from equilateral triangles.

Draw one line of symmetry on each shape.

Use a ruler.

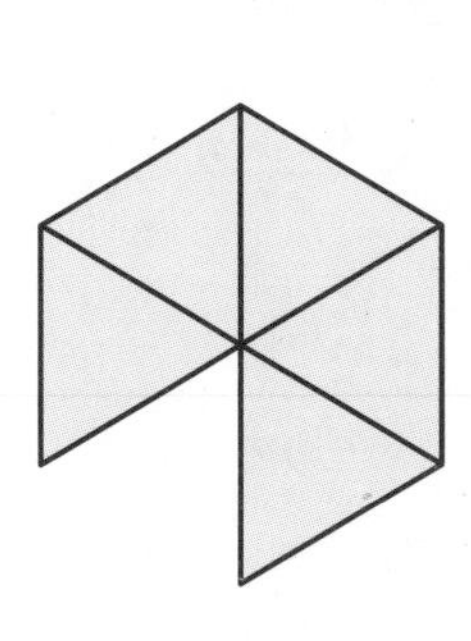

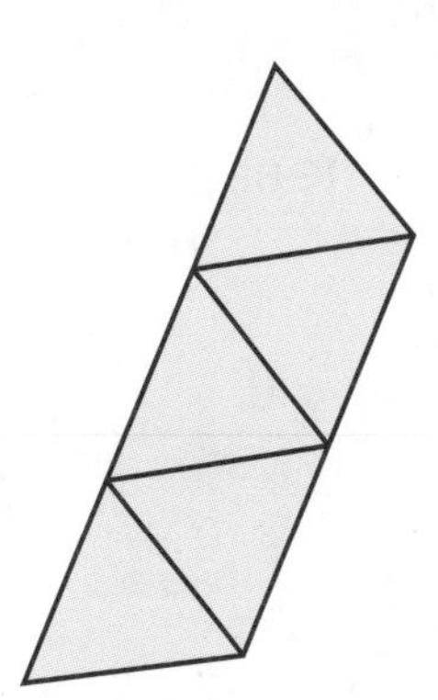

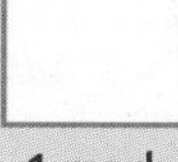

1 mark

/4

Total for this page

11 This table shows the mass of some fruit and vegetables.

Complete the table.

Fruits and vegetables	Grams	Kilograms
potatoes	5,500	5.5
apples		2.5
grapes		0.35
ginger	60	

2 marks

12 Here is an isosceles triangle.

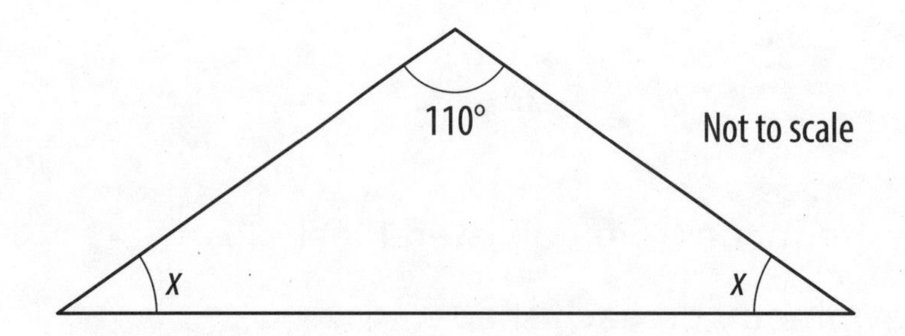

Calculate the size of angle x.

Do **not** use a protractor (angle measurer). [ ]°

1 mark

/3
Total for this page

13 Write the missing numbers to make these calculations correct.

a) $400 \times \square - 400 = 400$

1 mark

b) $(300 - \square) \times 300 = 600$

1 mark

14 Freya uses ribbon to make rosettes and a **3 metre** finishing line for a running race.

She uses this formula to work out the length of ribbon she needs altogether.

Total ribbon = number of rosettes × 50 cm + 3 m

a) Use the formula to calculate the length of ribbon she will need for a race with 10 rosettes.

[ ] m

1 mark

b) Freya buys 12 metres of ribbon.

Use the formula to calculate how many rosettes Freya can make for a race.

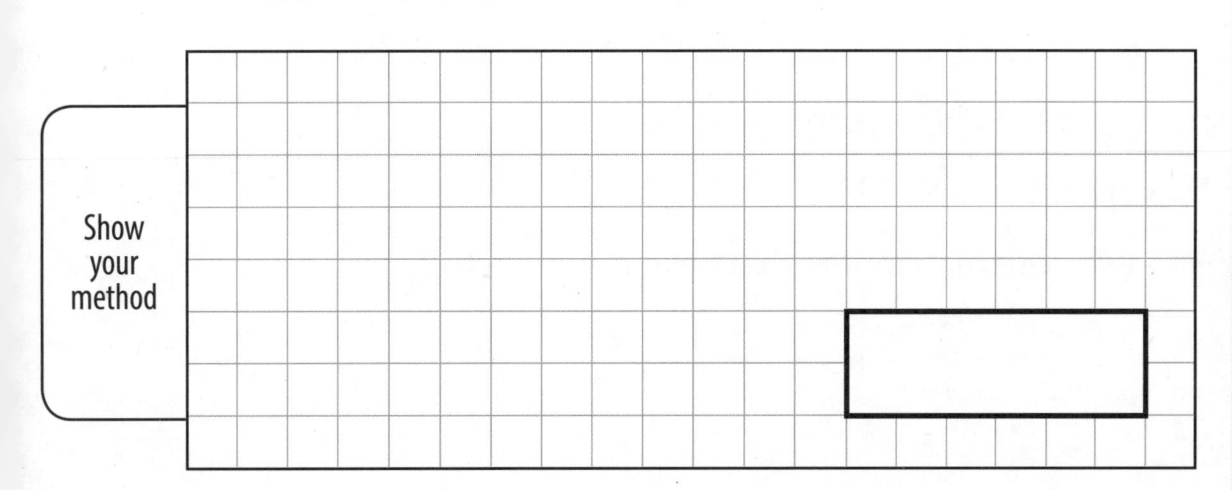

2 marks

/5

Total for this page

15 Use the digit cards to complete the subtraction calculation.

Each card can be used only once.

6 8 2 0 5 9

☐☐☐ – ☐☐☐ = 385

1 mark

16 The pie chart compares the amount of different fruit juices sold at a café.

lime
orange
lemon
apple

The café owner thinks that the amount of lime and lemon juice sold altogether is equal to the amount of orange juice sold.

Do you agree?

Circle your answer. YES / NO

Explain your answer.

1 mark

17 36 and 64 are both square numbers.

They have a sum of 100

Find two **square** numbers that have a sum of **160**

☐ and ☐

1 mark

/3

Total for this page

18 Round 3.485:

a) to the nearest whole number [ ]

b) to the nearest tenth ($\frac{1}{10}$) [ ]

c) to the nearest hundredth ($\frac{1}{100}$) [ ]

1 mark

19 Purba draws an isosceles triangle.

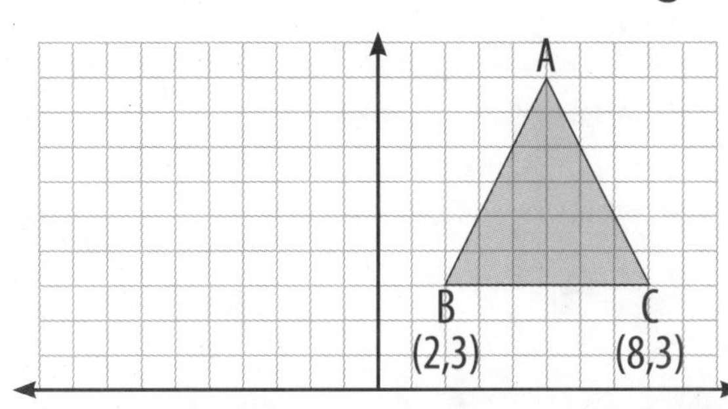

a) Write the coordinates of vertex **A**. (,)

1 mark

b) Purba translates the triangle 6 squares left and 2 squares down.

Write the coordinates of vertex **B** and vertex **C** **after** the translation.

B (,) **C** (,)

1 mark

/3

Total for this page

20 Gemma uses a map to plan her journey.

On the map, the distance of her journey is 25 cm.

The scale on the map is 2.5 cm = 5 km.

How far will Gemma travel on her journey? [ ] km

1 mark

21

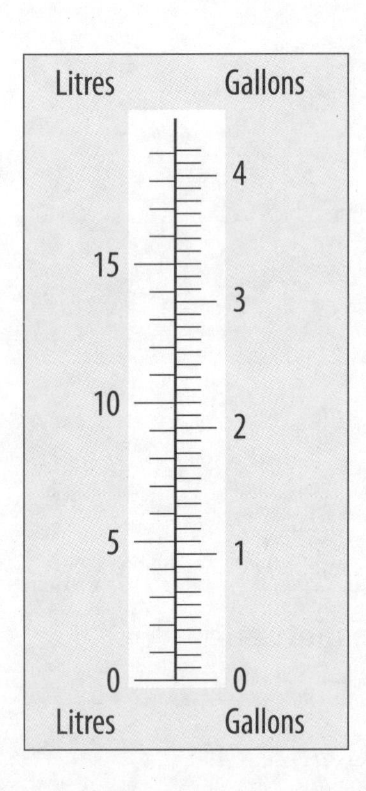

a) Approximately how many **litres** are there in **2 gallons**?

Give your answer to the nearest litre. [ ] litres

1 mark

b) Approximately how many **gallons** are there in **5 litres**?

Give your answer to **1 decimal place**. [ ] gallons

1 mark

/3

Total for this page

22 The black square has sides of 750 mm.

Calculate the radius of the circle in **cm**.

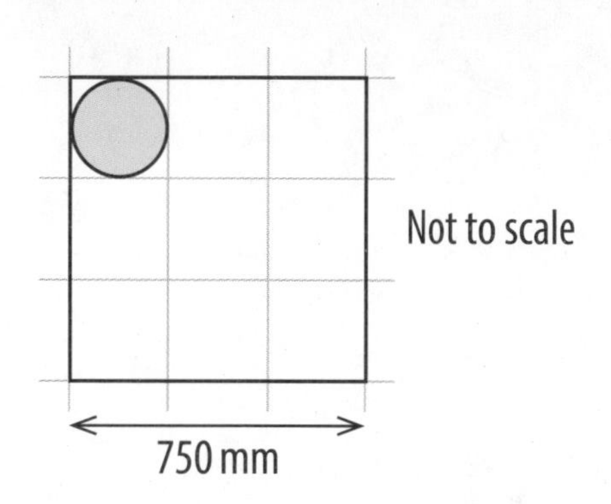

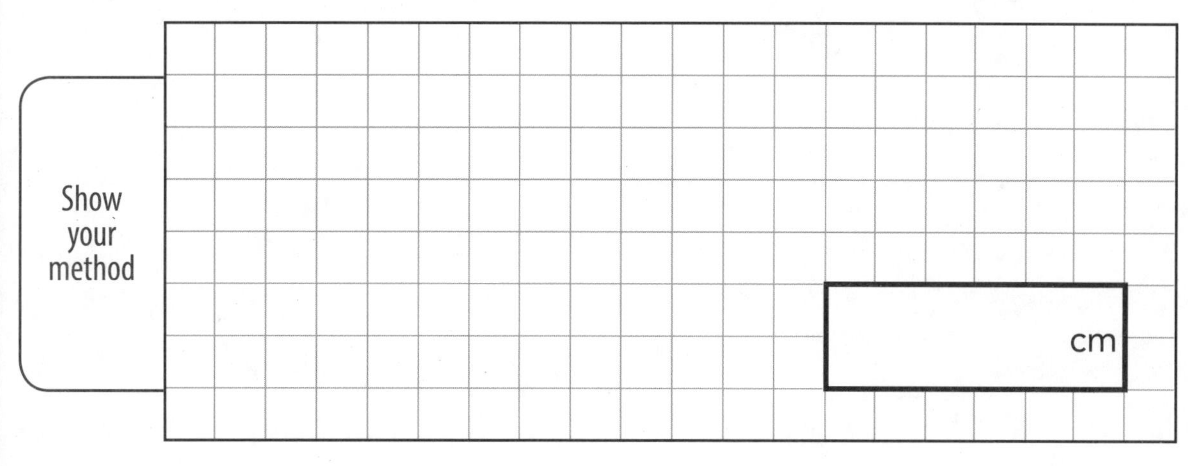

2 marks

23 Lena uses these symbols to show an equivalence.

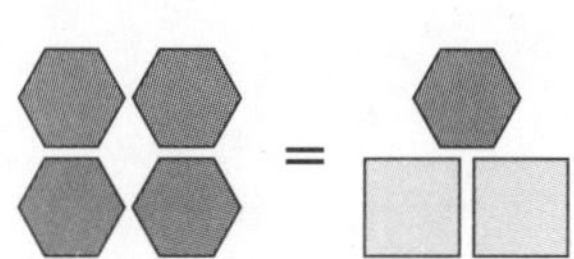

The value of ▭ is 1.2

Calculate the value of ⬢.

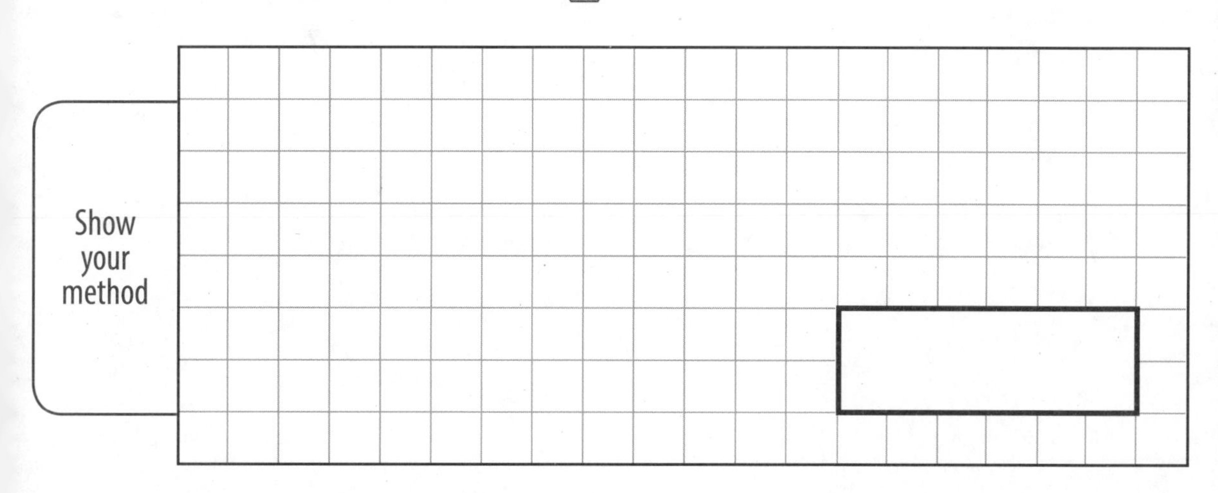

2 marks

/4

Total for this page

ACHIEVE

Year 6

Grammar, Spelling and Punctuation

SATs Practice Papers

Marie Lallaway
& Madeleine Barnes

RISING STARS

Introduction

About the Practice Papers for Grammar, Punctuation and Spelling

The tests are written to cover the content domain of the *Key Stage 2 English grammar, punctuation and spelling test framework for the National Curriculum tests from 2016* (Standards & Testing Agency, 2015). The tests **as a whole** provide complete coverage of the content domain.

There are six papers in total: three assessing grammar, punctuation and vocabulary strategies (as per *Paper 1: questions* from the National Tests) and three assessing spelling (as per *Paper 2: spelling* from the National Tests).

The tests are intended for use during the spring and summer terms of Year 6 in preparation for the National Tests. Test demand increases within each test, as in the National Tests, so initial questions are easier than those towards the end of each test.

How to use the Practice Papers

Preparation and timings

1. Help your child prepare for each paper by simulating test conditions.
2. Ensure your child is seated appropriately in front of the paper they are going to work on.
3. Your child will need pens or pencils and erasers.
4. There are no time limits for the tests but you should be guided by the timings of the actual tests in relation to the number of marks available. Help with reading may be given using the same rules as when providing a reader with the Key Stage 2 tests.

Spelling task: Introduce your child to the test by telling them that you will read out each sentence including the missing word. You will then say the missing word. Finally, you will repeat the whole sentence.

- Your child will need to write the missing words in the spaces on their answer sheets.
- Your child should make their best attempts at the spelling, even for words that may be unfamiliar.
- The full scripts for the spelling tests are provided in the answer section which can be found in a pull-out section in the middle of this book.

Supporting children during the tests

Before the tests, explain to your child that each test is an opportunity to show what they know, understand and can do. They should try to answer all the questions but should not worry if there are some they can't do.

Many children will be able to work independently in the tests, with minimal support. However, children should be encouraged to 'have a go' at a question, or to move on to a fresh question if they appear to be stuck. If they have time at the end of the test, they can come back to questions they have missed out.

Marking the tests

Use the mark scheme and your own judgement to award marks. Do not award half marks. Note that a number of questions in each test may require children to do more than one thing for one mark. The mark scheme provides clear guidance in the allocation of marks to support consistent marking of the tests.

It is useful for your child to mark their own test questions from time to time. Your child can look at the test sheets and mark them as you read out the question and answer. You will need to check that your child is marking accurately. This approach also provides an opportunity to recap on any questions that your child found difficult to answer.

Further guidance on marking is available on page 126.

Keep track of your child's score using the table on the inside back cover of this book.

Name:	Class:	Date:	Total marks: /50

Test 1, Paper 1: questions

1 Circle the words that should have **capital letters** in the sentence below.

1 mark

Each year in april, we take gifts to our grandparents in scotland for their birthdays.

2 Tick one box in each row to show whether the sentence is a **statement** or a **command**.

1 mark

Sentence	Statement	Command
Today, the train will leave earlier than usual.		
Tomorrow, go to your grandma's after school.		
Yesterday, we climbed a tree.		
Bring your sports kit for the match this afternoon.		

3 Circle the **relative pronoun** in the sentence below.

1 mark

The new girl who started our school today is coming to our house later.

/3

Total for this page

4 Which **preposition** can complete both sentences?

Write the preposition in the box below.

1 mark

I travel ______________ home to school on the bus each day.

You must follow the treasure hunt clues ______________ the start to the finish.

word: [ ]

5 What is the grammatical term for the underlined word?

1 mark

Anita's idea was interesting but <u>impossible</u>.

Tick **one**.

noun ☐

adjective ☐

adverb ☐

preposition ☐

6 Underline the longest possible **noun phrase** in the sentence below.

1 mark

Have you seen the new climbing frame in the playground?

/3

Total for this page

7 Circle the correct **verb form** to complete the sentence below.

are being **have been** **are** **will have been**

Max and Jensen ____________________ best friends since they started school.

1 mark

8 Write the question below as a **command**.

Remember to punctuate your answer correctly.

Can you open the window as it is very hot?

____

1 mark

9 Circle all the **nouns** in the sentence below.

Jess was asked to share her ideas about having more healthy food in school.

1 mark

/3

Total for this page

10 Rewrite the sentence below, using correct **capital letters**.

1 mark

on monday we will visit buckingham palace.

____

11 Circle the correct **verb forms** to complete these sentences.

1 mark

is working / has worked / worked

Mr Oliver ______________ in the factory since it first opened and is still here today.

tries / has tried / tried

Samara ______________ her best in the races yesterday.

make / have made / making

We ______________ cakes to share with you all now.

12 Underline the **objects** in the sentences below.

1 mark

Holly threw the ball.

Grandad pushed the wheelbarrow.

Can you catch it?

/3

Total for this page

13 Insert a **subordinating conjunction** to show that we swam in the river and played games at the same time.

We played games ________________ we swam in the river.

1 mark

14 Circle all the **pronouns** in the sentence below.

Oscar made a model castle from old boxes his dad had given him.

1 mark

15 Insert a **comma** in the correct place in the sentence below.

Full of wonder we all gazed at the shooting star.

1 mark

/3

Total for this page

16 Draw a line to match each word with its **synonym**.

swift	secure
fasten	concern
immerse	soak
issue	rapid

1 mark

17 Tick one box in each row to show whether the sentences are written in the **active** or the **passive voice**.

Sentence	Active	Passive
The seals were fed from a bucket of fish.		
Kangaroos use their tails to balance.		
Some trees are planted by squirrels burying nuts.		

1 mark

18 Draw a line to match each **prefix** with the correct word.

im	legal
ir	possible
in	responsible
il	attentive

1 mark

/3

Total for this page

19 Which is the correct way to write the sentence below as **reported speech**?

1 mark

"Butterflies can see only three colours," said Anna.

Tick **one**.

Anna said, that butterflies could see only three colours. ☐

Anna said that "butterflies can see only three colours." ☐

Anna says "that butterflies can see only three colours." ☐

Anna said that butterflies can see only three colours. ☐

20 Rewrite the sentence below using **Standard English** to correct the underlined word.

1 mark

Remember to punctuate your answer correctly.

Can I have one of <u>them</u> cakes?

____

21 Circle the word that shows the event is **most likely** to happen.

1 mark

definitely **perhaps** **possibly** **probably**

Nafeesah will ______________ become an acrobat when she grows up.

/3

Total for this page

22 Add an **adverbial phrase** to the sentence below.

________________________________, I always clean my teeth.

1 mark

23 Tick the box to show which part of this sentence is a **relative clause**.

Long, long ago | there lived | a wonderful, flying creature | that guarded the magical mountain.

☐ ☐ ☐ ☐

1 mark

24 What is the grammatical term for the underlined words in the sentence below?

The storm caused a lot of damage when it struck last night.

Tick **one**.

as a main clause ☐

as a noun phrase ☐

as a preposition phrase ☐

as a relative clause ☐

1 mark

/3

Total for this page

25 Write the **contracted form** of the underlined words in the box.

"You should have gone to bed earlier," my mum said.

1 mark

26 Rewrite the sentence below as **direct speech**.

Remember to punctuate your sentence correctly.

The scientist said that she was pleased with her discovery.

1 mark

27 Tick the **verb** that is written in the **past progressive form** in the passage below.

The stars were twinkling in the sky as Jodie gazed upwards and made a wish. It had been a lovely day.

1 mark

/3

Total for this page

28 Insert a **semi-colon** in the correct place in the sentence below.

There was a parade in the road outside school we all went out to have a look.

1 mark

29 In the sentence below, Dad planted the flowers in the garden before the dog dug them up.

Write the verb in the **past perfect form** in the gap.

to plant

In the morning, Dad ____________ lots of new flowers in the garden but the dog dug them up looking for its buried bone.

1 mark

30 Explain how removing the **comma** changes the meaning of the sentence.

Let's play chase, Kate.

Let's play chase Kate.

____

____

____

1 mark

/3

Total for this page

31 Add the correct word from the box to complete the sentence below in the **subjunctive form.**

1 mark

listened
listen
listening
listens

The flying instructor recommended that Josh ______________ carefully to all the information.

32 Tick one sentence that is correctly punctuated.

1 mark

Tick **one**.

Venus – the brightest planet in our sky – can sometimes be seen without a telescope. ☐

The tallest volcano – at 27 km high, in fact – in the Solar System is on Mars. ☐

In 1846 – Neptune, the planet – was discovered. ☐

Many astronomers – believe that Mercury – was once a much larger planet. ☐

/2

Total for this page

33 Tick the option that must end with an **exclamation mark**.

1 mark

Tick **one**.

Give it to me ☐

Can you believe that we won ☐

What an amazing friend you are ☐

Sit down ☐

34 Circle the word in the passage that contains an apostrophe for **possession**.

1 mark

Now that he's here, I'll book the taxi. We can pick up Elsie from Fred's house.

35 Circle the **two** words that are **antonyms** in the sentence below.

1 mark

The teacher completed the register to record who was present or absent.

/3

Total for this page

36 Which sentence is written using **Standard English**?

Tick **one**.

I done my exercises in the park. ☐

They was all late for assembly. ☐

I swam with the school team in the competition. ☐

You been here for three hours. ☐

1 mark

37 What is the **word class** of the underlined words in the sentence below?

The boy put three drinks in a bag.

____

1 mark

38 Replace the underlined word or words in the sentence below with the correct **pronouns**.

Mr Lavin told the children to line up and Mr Lavin checked that

☐

the children were all there.

☐

1 mark

/3

Total for this page

39 What is the **subject** of the sentence below?

Last Wednesday, Luke went to Manchester to see Ellie.

Tick **one**.

Wednesday ☐

Manchester ☐

Luke ☐

Ellie ☐

1 mark

40 Circle the **relative pronoun** in the sentence below.

My uncle, who was a famous ice-skater, has moved to America.

1 mark

41 Rearrange the words in the statement below to make it a **question**.

Use only the given words.

Remember to punctuate your sentence correctly.

Statement: They are waiting for the train.

Question: ______________________________

1 mark

/3

Total for this page

42 Which sentence uses the **colon** correctly?

1 mark

Tick **one**.

I bought: some new stationery pencils, a ruler, a selection of pens and a pencil case. ☐

I bought some new stationery: pencils, a ruler, a selection of pens and a pencil case. ☐

I bought some new: stationery pencils, a ruler, a selection of pens and a pencil case. ☐

I bought some new stationery pencils: a ruler, a selection of pens and a pencil case. ☐

43 Tick **two** boxes to show where the **inverted commas** should go.

1 mark

☐ Freddie told me to put it there ☐, interrupted ☐ Pritika ☐.

44 Which underlined group of words is a **subordinate clause**?

1 mark

Tick **one**.

<u>This is the best place</u> I have ever been. ☐

<u>Because you are late</u>, we have changed the song! ☐

I didn't want to stay in the hotel <u>for three days</u>. ☐

Would you like a drink of <u>milk or water</u>? ☐

/3

Total for this page

45 Which **punctuation mark** should be used in the place indicated by the arrow?

1 mark

Aradhya loved many different sports ☐ her favourites were swimming and tennis.

Tick **one**.

comma	☐
semi-colon	☐
full stop	☐
hyphen	☐

46 Circle the **adverb** in the sentence below.

1 mark

We are hoping to visit Gran's lovely home soon.

47 Insert one **comma** in the correct place in the sentence below.

1 mark

Last Wednesday we won the singing competition at the town hall.

/3

Total for this page

48 Insert a pair of **brackets** in the correct place in the sentence below.

1 mark

The largest river in the world is the Amazon River 6,992 km in South America.

49 Complete each sentence below with a word formed from the root word enjoy.

1 mark

The party was a very ______________ experience.

She got incredible ______________ from reading adventure stories.

50 Circle the two **conjunctions** in the sentence below.

1 mark

I really wanted to go to the concert, but I realised that I didn't have my ticket or my phone with me!

/3

Total for this page

Name:	Class:	Date:	Total marks: /20

Test 1, Paper 2: spelling

1 We are ________________ the bulbs from their pots to the garden.

2 There was a ________________ response to your idea.

3 The new road has made a ________________ difference to the traffic problem.

4 To bake bread, you first need to make a ________________.

5 We have designed an ________________ programme for the concert.

6 Our snake is growing in ________________ each month.

7 The ________________ has introduced a new law.

8 My favourite book is full of ________________ stories.

9 Your dentist will ________________ you on how to care for your teeth.

10 It is helpful if your dog is trained to be ________________.

11 There was an ________________ pause after Tom's joke.

12 The rope should be ________________ up tidily after you use it.

13 It is ________________ to wear a safety helmet in the caves.

14 They ________________ through the night to arrive on time.

15 That is a lovely ________________ of fabric.

16 There was a ________________ smell in the garden shed.

17 I went to the doctor because I had a ________________.

18 When I was on holiday, we sailed to an ________________.

19 It is very important that you eat a ________________ lunch.

20 My Dad found the idea quite ________________.

Name:	Class:	Date:	Total marks: /50

Test 2, Paper 1: questions

1 Write the **contracted form** of the underlined words in the box.

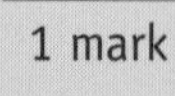

1 mark

I told Joe that he had won first prize.

2 Circle the words in the sentence that should have **capital letters**.

1 mark

On friday we will go to molly's house for tea.

3 Insert an appropriate **adverb** to complete the sentence below.

1 mark

The ducklings swam ______________ across the pond.

/3

Total for this page

4 Tick the sentences that correctly use the **possessive apostrophe**.

1 mark

Can I borrow Jamila's bicycle? ☐

At the start of the race, all of the cars' engines were revving noisily. ☐

The dog has lost it's ball. ☐

After the match, the teams' kit was filthy. ☐

5 Tick the box to show where a **comma** should go.

1 mark

If ☐ you enjoy dancing ☐ you should come to the theatre ☐ with ☐ us this evening.

6 Complete the sentences below by writing the **conjunctions** from the box in the correct place.

1 mark

Use each conjunction only once.

but	or	and

Would you like to play inside ______________ outside?

You will need a drink ______________ a ticket, ______________ you do not need to pay for them.

/3

Total for this page

7 Underline all the **verbs** in the sentence below.

Female lions do most of the hunting while the males patrol the territory and protect the group.

1 mark

8 Write the correct **determiner**, a or an, in each gap below.

On our holiday, we arrived at ______________ airport in the middle of nowhere and we were picked up by ______________ ox and cart to take us to ______________ train station.

1 mark

9 Circle the verb in the **past perfect tense** to complete the sentence below.

When I arrived at the cinema, the film **started / had started / was starting / starts**.

1 mark

/3

Total for this page

10 Which option is the correct **relative pronoun** for the sentence below?

1 mark

The town ______________ I live is close to the sea.

Tick **one**.

that ☐

where ☐

which ☐

who ☐

11 Write the verbs in the gaps in the **past progressive tense**.

1 mark

to listen

Simon and Nikhil ______________ to the radio while they

to build

______________ a model plane.

12 Which sentence is the most **formal**?

1 mark

Tick **one**.

Daily exercise should be promoted for all. ☐

You should exercise every day. ☐

Exercising every day is a great idea. ☐

You really should try to exercise daily. ☐

/3

Total for this page

13 Tick **two** boxes to show where the **inverted commas** should go.

1 mark

The mayor announced, This year's carnival procession will

travel throughout the whole town.

14 Label the boxes with **N** (**noun**), **A** (**adjective**), **V** (**verb**) and **P** (**preposition**) to show the parts of the sentence.

1 mark

"After the storm, the destruction left in the garden was

completely awful," said one local.

15 Explain why an **apostrophe** is used in the sentence below.

1 mark

Everyone in the class liked Oscar's idea.

____

____

/3

Total for this page

16 Draw a line to match each word with its **suffix**.

appoint	ful
bitter	less
hair	ness
dread	ment

1 mark

17 Elsie wants to know if the team are in the final round.

Write the **question** she could ask to find out.

Remember to punctuate your sentence correctly.

____

1 mark

18 Underline one word in each sentence that shows that it is a **command**.

When the race starts, run as fast as you can.

If the alarm sounds, leave the building quickly and quietly.

1 mark

/3

Total for this page

19 Why is a **comma** used in the sentence below?

Would you like to go to the park, the museum or the cinema?

1 mark

Tick **one**.

to divide the sentence in two halves ☐

to introduce speech ☐

to mark a clause ☐

to separate items in a list ☐

20 Which word is the **antonym** of <u>combine</u>?

1 mark

Tick **one**.

separate ☐

mix ☐

comfort ☐

descend ☐

21 Underline the **subject** of the sentence below.

The football manager posed for a photograph.

1 mark

/3

Total for this page

22 Which sentence below is correctly punctuated?

1 mark

Tick **one**.

We saw beautiful landscapes: on our trip, mountains, lakes and coasts. ☐

We saw beautiful landscapes on our trip: mountains, lakes and coasts. ☐

We saw: beautiful landscapes on our trip, mountains, lakes and coasts. ☐

We saw beautiful landscapes on our trip, mountains: lakes and coasts. ☐

23 Which sentence is a **command**?

1 mark

Tick **one**.

I am bringing a packed lunch. ☐

You should bring a packed lunch. ☐

Bring a packed lunch so you do not get hungry. ☐

You will need a packed lunch so you do not get hungry. ☐

24 Circle the **subordinate clause** in the sentence below.

1 mark

I would love to swim with dolphins even though it might be a little scary at first.

/3

Total for this page

25 Which sentences below use before as a **subordinating conjunction**?

1 mark

Tick **two**.

Let's go to the swimming pool before lunch. ☐

I'd like to finish my book before we go out. ☐

Can we practise our dance again before the performance? ☐

The phone stopped ringing before I could answer it. ☐

26 Circle all the **pronouns** in the passage below.

1 mark

Archie took a lot of care with his toys. He was annoyed because one of them had been broken by a friend.

27 Match the words below with their **synonyms**.

1 mark

influence	imprison
courteous	polite
confine	persuade
accusation	gratitude
thanks	blame

/3

Total for this page

28 What is the **word class** of each underlined word?

Baljit drew a careful picture. ____________

Baljit draws carefully. ____________

1 mark

29 The audience finished their applause for the magician before the singer began.

Complete the sentence below with the correct **verb form**.

The audience ____________ finished applauding the musician just as the singer took her place on stage.

1 mark

30 Which sentence below uses the **subjunctive form**?

Tick **one**.

Everyone in our family would like to go on an African safari. ☐

I would drive more slowly if I were you. ☐

Josh will meet you at the front of the swimming pool. ☐

Musah would like to have a new bike for his birthday. ☐

1 mark

/3

Total for this page

31 Underline the **adverbial phrase** in the sentence below.

During the match, Katie scored two amazing goals.

1 mark

32 Priya is making a collage picture. She needs to use scissors, coloured paper and glue.

Finish the instructions below, writing the equipment as a list with **bullet points**.

Remember to punctuate your answer correctly.

To make a collage, you will need this equipment:

- ______________________
- ______________________
- ______________________

1 mark

33 What is the **word class** of the underlined words?

<u>We</u> waited patiently for <u>him</u> as <u>he</u> was really late.

Tick **one**.

prepositions	☐
verbs	☐
pronouns	☐
nouns	☐

1 mark

/3

Total for this page

34 Write the verbs in the gaps in the **simple past tense**.

1 mark

to walk

The bus didn't come so we ______________ to school.

to sing **to bring**

My friend ______________ with the choir while I ______________ more chairs for the audience to sit on.

35 Which sentence uses **capital letters** correctly?

1 mark

Tick **one**.

The Teacher took the children to the library in the middle of Newcastle. ☐

The teacher took the children to the Library in the middle of newcastle. ☐

The Teacher took the children to the Library in the middle of Newcastle. ☐

The teacher took the children to the library in the middle of Newcastle. ☐

36 Tick the option that must end with a **question mark**.

1 mark

Tick **one**.

Ask me what time it opens at ☐

Can you tell me what time it opens at ☐

What time it opens at is written on the sign ☐

I will ask what time it opens at ☐

/3

Total for this page

37 Circle the **possessive pronoun** in the passage below.

When I visited the new school, a girl showed me where her locker was.

1 mark

38 What is the grammatical term for the underlined words in the sentence below?

She carried the heavy wooden chest with a gold handle into the kitchen.

____

1 mark

39 Which sentence uses the word light as a **verb**?

Tick **one**.

There was a very bright light in the distance. ☐

Can you light the candles please? ☐

I need a new light for the kitchen. ☐

The light was on all night. ☐

1 mark

/3

Total for this page

40 Draw a line to match each sentence to its correct **function**. Use each function box only once.

1 mark

Sentence	Function
You have been to that art gallery, haven't you	command
The art gallery is open now	exclamation
How amazing the art is in this gallery	statement
Go into the gift shop in the gallery	question

41 Which one **prefix** can be added to all three words below to make their **antonyms**?

1 mark

Write the prefix in the box.

mature
moral
patient

42 Which two sentences contain a **preposition**?

1 mark

Tick **two**.

She happily watched the concert. ☐

He walked across the road. ☐

The books were arranged neatly. ☐

We struggled to climb over the fence. ☐

/3

Total for this page

43a What is the name of the **punctuation marks** on either side of the words which was broken in the sentence below?

1 mark

Dad put the bottle, which was broken, into the bin.

____

43b What is the name of a **different** punctuation mark that could be used correctly in the same places?

1 mark

____

44 Insert a **semi-colon** in the correct place in the sentence below.

1 mark

There will be a huge celebration party next week it will probably be on Monday.

/3

Total for this page

45 Write a **noun phrase** containing at least three words to complete the sentence below.

Remember to punctuate your sentence correctly.

______________________ is coming to my party on Wednesday.

1 mark

46 Circle the **possessive pronoun** in the sentence below.

Luke took some of Ellie's sweets and then pretended that they were his.

1 mark

47 Rewrite the sentence below so that it is in the **active voice**.

Remember to punctuate your sentence correctly.

The seeds were planted by the children.

____

1 mark

/3

Total for this page

48 Circle the **two** words that are **synonyms** in the passage below.

1 mark

Many of the items in the shop were overpriced. They tried to find some more reasonable gifts, but left feeling everything was extortionate.

49 Which sentence uses the **present perfect form**?

1 mark

Tick **one**.

My dog was unwell, but since he has been at the vet's, he is much better. ☐

He was feeling excited when he won the cup. ☐

The children hung up their coats and sat in their seats. ☐

They are playing their instruments in the orchestra this evening. ☐

/2

Total for this page

Name:	Class:	Date:	Total marks: /20

Test 2, Paper 2: spelling

1 That jacket is too ____________ to wear.

2 Our ____________ are all getting together for a big meal.

3 It is important to care for the ____________.

4 The same bird keeps ____________ at my window.

5 There are ____________ trees of a hundred years old in the park.

6 The bridge ____________ during the flood.

7 James made a ____________ effort to work harder.

8 It would be ____________ to make a mistake on purpose.

9 I need a ____________ because I'm going to sneeze.

10 This spicy food is making my ____________ tingle.

11 Even a cold can be ____________.

12 You will meet the ____________ of judges before the competition.

13 This class has a good ____________ record.

14 Sam's writing is so small it is almost ____________.

15 The twins ____________ lots of gifts for their birthday.

16 The guide told us not to walk any ____________.

17 A ____________ author is coming to our school next month.

18 The ____________ presented her designs to the council.

19 Leave space for your ____________ at the end of the letter.

20 We looked at the family tree to identify who Prince Charles was a ____________ of.

Name:	Class:	Date:	Total marks: /50

Test 3, Paper 1: questions

1 Which of the sentences below have a **capital letter** missing?

1 mark

Tick **two**.

We often build snowmen in the winter. ☐

I went to see the dentist about my toothache. ☐

The pyrenees is a range of mountains in Spain. ☐

One of England's coasts faces the atlantic Ocean. ☐

2 Circle all the **verbs** in the sentence below.

1 mark

Traffic stood still as the procession passed through the centre of town.

3 Add a question tag at the end of the sentence below to make it a **question**.

1 mark

Sarah hasn't arrived yet, ______________ ______________?

/3

Total for this page

4 Label the boxes with **D** (**determiner**), **A** (**adverb**), **N** (**noun**) or **P** (**preposition**) to show the parts of the sentence.

Now our river is much cleaner, otters have come back to live in the area.

1 mark

5 Circle all the **conjunctions** in the passage below.

The explorers had followed the path until they met a river. As they could not cross it, they sat down on the bank while they considered a plan.

1 mark

6 Label the boxes with **S** (**subject**) or **O** (**object**) in the sentences below.

The cows are contentedly munching grass in their field.

We shook the rattle and the baby laughed.

1 mark

/3

Total for this page

7 Add two **commas** to the sentence below to make it clear that Pam has four hobbies.

Pam's hobbies are swimming cycling reading and listening to music.

1 mark

8 Tick all the sentences that correctly use **apostrophes**.

Teri didn't like the snake's at the zoo.	☐
Ahmed always enjoy's eating biscuits and cakes.	☐
They hadn't visited Henry's house before.	☐
It's time to go home now.	☐

1 mark

9 Write a **noun phrase** containing at least three words to complete the sentence below.

Remember to punctuate your sentence correctly.

______________________ has moved in next door to us.

1 mark

/3

Total for this page

10 Circle all the **determiners** in the passage below.

Do we have any biscuits in the cupboard? If there is a packet, can I have some?

1 mark

11 Which of the events in the sentences below is **most likely** to happen?

1 mark

Tick **one**.

We could build a tunnel through the mountain. ☐

They might be able to cross the river further downstream. ☐

I will travel by plane in the morning. ☐

She may call you this weekend. ☐

12 Which option correctly introduces the **subordinate clause** in the sentence below?

1 mark

The winter's evening was very cold indeed ______________ the fire was burning brightly to try to keep us warm.

Tick **one**.

in addition ☐

instead of ☐

although ☐

however ☐

/3

Total for this page

13 Tick one box in each row to show whether the sentences are written in the **active voice** or the **passive voice**.

1 mark

Sentence	Active	Passive
All of the paintings in the museum had been stolen.		
The thief entered through an open window.		
Some of the pictures were recovered by the police.		
Unfortunately, the robber escaped with the best ones.		

14 Which sentence is correctly punctuated?

1 mark

Tick **one**.

"Will everyone please listen? requested Meera." ☐

"Will everyone please listen? requested" Meera. ☐

"Will everyone please listen"? requested Meera. ☐

"Will everyone please listen?" requested Meera. ☐

15 Why is a **comma** used in the sentence below?

1 mark

Whenever we go for a walk at the coast, we collect interesting shells and stones in a bucket.

Tick **one**.

to separate items in a list ☐

to divide the sentence in half ☐

to mark the end of a clause ☐

to join two sentences together ☐

/3

Total for this page

16 Tick two sentences that include verbs in the **present progressive form**.

1 mark

Tick **two**.

Ants have six legs and each leg has six joints.	☐
Although tiny, ants can lift 20 times their own body weight.	☐
Ants are marching across the floor of my kitchen.	☐
Marcus is sitting on the grass to watch the ants carrying leaves to their nest.	☐

17 Draw a line to match the correct **prefix** with each of the words below.

1 mark

mis	integrate
dis	look
over	lead
un	necessary

18 Tick one box to show the sentence that describes the houses that are 300 years old.

1 mark

Tick **one**.

There are 300 year-old houses in my street.	☐
There are 300 year old houses in my street.	☐
There are 300-year-old houses in my street.	☐
There are 300 year old-houses in my street.	☐

/3

Total for this page

19 Insert a **colon** in the correct place to the sentence below.

We have a number of people visiting this weekend aunts, uncles, grandparents and cousins.

1 mark

20 Rewrite the two sentences below as one sentence using an appropriate **coordinating conjunction**.

Remember to punctuate your answer correctly.

You can go to the cinema. You will need to be home by 9pm.

____

1 mark

21 Tick one box to show which **pronouns** should complete this sentence.

The instructions were so difficult to follow that he had to ask __________ brother to help __________ with __________.

1 mark

Tick **one**.

he	her	those	☐
his	him	them	☐
her	them	it	☐
my	his	they	☐

/3

Total for this page

22 Explain why the words underlined are placed between a pair of **commas**.

1 mark

My cousin, who used to work in India, is moving to a new job in England.

____

____

____

23 Add a **suffix** to change the word forgive into a noun.

1 mark

I will forgive you.

You have my forgive ____________.

24 Which of the sentences below correctly uses a **single dash**?

1 mark

Tick **one**.

The tiger is the biggest species of the cat family – it can reach lengths of up to 3.3 metres.	☐
Tigers are endangered by hunting – and destruction of their environments.	☐
Tiger cubs leave their mothers – at about two years old.	☐
Tigers can reach speeds of up to 40 miles an hour – when hunting.	☐

/3

Total for this page

25 Tick one box in each row to show whether a **semi-colon** is used correctly or incorrectly.

1 mark

Sentence	Correct	Incorrect
Trekking through a jungle can be very hard work; pushing through bushes, climbing over creepers.		
The tops of mountains can have extreme climates; they can be extremely hot, or extremely cold.		
Surprisingly, a desert supports many types of plant; and wildlife.		

26 Rewrite the underlined verb in the **past progressive**.

1 mark

While we <u>to run</u> for the bus, I tripped and fell.

27 Rewrite the sentence below, using the **passive voice**.

1 mark

Remember to punctuate your answer correctly.

Alex played a lovely solo on the piano.

/3

Total for this page

28 Explain how the word <u>might</u> changes the meaning of the sentence.

1 mark

I will practise my spellings before the test.

I <u>might</u> practise my spellings before the test.

____

____

____

29 Correctly insert a pair of **brackets** in the sentence below.

1 mark

Golden eagles have been known to attack a variety of large animals foxes, wild cats, deer and even goats using their large talons and beaks.

30 Tick the words that mean the same as <u>envelop</u>.

1 mark

		Tick **one**.
cover	surround	☐
send	communicate	☐
locate	find	☐
present	display	☐

/3

Total for this page

31 Underline the **subordinate clause** in the sentence below.

Some lizards can detach their tails if they are caught by predators.

1 mark

32 Tick one box in each row to show whether the word after is used as a **subordinating conjunction** or as a **preposition**.

Sentence	Subordinating conjunction	Preposition
Shall we go to the museum after we have seen the castle?		
The concert will begin after everyone has sat down.		
Let's make some cakes after school today.		

1 mark

33 Draw a line to match each sentence to the correct **determiner**.

Use each determiner only **once**.

We went to a farm and I collected _______ apple.	the
We all had _______ fantastic time.	a
I hope we can go to _______ farm again.	an

1 mark

/3

Total for this page

34 What is the **word class** of the underlined words in the sentence below?

1 mark

We saw a very unusual <u>bird</u> while on holiday in <u>Wales</u>.

Tick **one**.

adjectives ☐

adverbs ☐

pronouns ☐

nouns ☐

35 Underline the **adverbial** in the sentence below.

1 mark

In November, our class will go away on a residential trip.

36 Replace the underlined words in the sentences below with their **expanded forms**.

1 mark

<u>He's</u> going to meet me after dinner, so <u>I'll</u> make sure I am on time.

_______________ _______________

I really <u>don't</u> want to be late.

____

/3

Total for this page

37 Tick the option that correctly completes the sentence below.

1 mark

__________ will take place on Fridays at 1:30 p.m.

Tick **one**.

After half-term swimming, lessons ☐

After half-term, swimming lessons ☐

After, half-term swimming lessons ☐

After half-term, swimming lessons, ☐

38 Complete the sentence with an appropriate **subordinating conjunction**.

1 mark

We cannot go swimming today __________ it is too cold.

39 Circle the **two** words that show the **tense** in the sentence below.

1 mark

The zoo was shut, so we went to the cinema instead.

/3

Total for this page

40 Underline the **relative clause** in the sentence below.

The girl who sits next to me is called Jackie.

1 mark

41 Which sentence uses the word point as a **verb**?

Tick **one**.

What was the point in that? ☐

My pencil has an extremely sharp point. ☐

Don't point, it's rude. ☐

Place the ruler next to the point. ☐

1 mark

42 Write a **command** which could be the first step in the instructions for getting ready for bed.

Remember to punctuate your answer correctly.

____

____

1 mark

/3

Total for this page

43 Which sentence is a **statement**?

Tick **one**.

Do not lift that equipment by yourself ☐

Be careful when you lift the equipment ☐

You can carry the equipment with a partner ☐

Do you know how to carry the equipment ☐

1 mark

44 Circle the **adverb** in the sentence below.

I really love to travel and hope I can go to Italy soon.

1 mark

45 Tick the option that must end with an **exclamation mark**.

Tick **one**.

How amazing that present is ☐

How did you manage to do that ☐

Give it to me ☐

Stand up ☐

1 mark

/3

Total for this page

46 Which **verb** completes the sentence so that it uses the **subjunctive form**?

1 mark

I wish I ______________ able to come, but I already have plans.

Tick **one**.

were ☐

be ☐

am ☐

was ☐

47 What is the grammatical term for the underlined words in the sentence below?

1 mark

The multi-coloured kites were very popular on the beach.

Tick **one**.

as an adverbial ☐

as a noun phrase ☐

as a subordinate clause ☐

as a fronted adverbial ☐

48 Complete the table below with the correct **singular** or **plural** form.

1 mark

one fox	→	seven ______________
one ______________	→	some lorries
one cactus	→	several ______________

/3

Total for this page

49 Tick one box in each row to show whether the sentence is written in the **active voice** or the **passive voice**.

1 mark

Sentence	Active	Passive
The girls won the trophy.		
Everybody was surprised when they won.		
The winning goal was scored by Jess.		

50 Which one **prefix** can be added to all three words below to make their **antonyms**?

1 mark

Write the prefix in the box.

understanding
read
spell

/2

Total for this page

Name:	Class:	Date:	Total marks: /20

Test 3, Paper 2: spelling

1 Everyone ____________________ at the end of the performance.

2 Jo had no ____________________ in climbing to the top of the rope.

3 That's a very ____________________ idea.

4 The park is ____________________ by bushes and trees.

5 We are ____________________ a massive collage in class.

6 That bag ____________________ too much for me to carry.

7 Charlie's idea was ____________________ to the discussion.

8 Anna carries her bag over her ____________________.

9 England has several ____________________ airports.

10 We will ____________________ have a roast dinner at the weekend.

11 If you have a phone in your ____________________, turn it off now.

12 I grazed my ____________________ when I fell over.

13 The Romans ____________________ much of Europe.

14 I am helping to make the ____________________ for the school play.

15 My ____________________ has lost her cat.

16 Since you have missed the train, I ____________________ you will be on time.

17 She ____________________ everything from the boxes into the new office.

18 It was a ____________________ week for Luke.

19 She had a ____________________ memory of her holiday in Spain.

20 After the residential, Sarah was known as the most ____________________ girl.

General guidance on marking Paper 1

Selected response questions

In questions where children must select the correct response or identify a feature from a given field of data (such as tick boxes and tables, circling or underlining of the answer, drawing lines to 'match' boxes, labelling, e.g. 'V' for 'verb'):

- Accept any unambiguous indication of the correct answer (e.g. answer circled rather than ticked; lines that do not touch the boxes, provided the intention is clear).
- Do not accept encircling/underlining of less than half of the required word.
- Do not accept ambiguous labelling (e.g. the use of 'AD' or 'A' where a distinction is required between 'adjective' and 'adverb').

Constructed response questions

In open questions or questions where children must transform a given word, phrase or sentence, or insert a word or phrase:

- Accept incorrect spellings of the correct response if no specific mark scheme guidance is given. Correct spelling is generally required for questions assessing contracted forms, plurals, verb tenses, prefixes and suffixes.
- Do not accept punctuation that is ambiguous or not recognisable as the required punctuation mark, for example if it is unclear whether the mark is a comma or full stop.
- When punctuating a sentence, do not accept answers in which capital letters are omitted or placed inappropriately in a sentence, or where an entire word is capitalised, nor answers where there is ambiguity in the comparative sizes of letters.
- Accept letters or punctuation marks that have been reversed, but which are still clearly identifiable.
- Accept correct answers that replace a crossed-out attempt, but not crossed-out answers, whether or not these have been replaced by a further attempt.

All question types

- Accept a correct answer given somewhere other than the answer space, providing it is not contradicted by another answer written elsewhere.
- Do not accept an answer when more than the required number of answers is given (e.g. both correct and incorrect responses given).

ACHIEVE

Year 6

Reading

SATs Practice Papers

Laura Collinson
& Shareen Mayers

RISING STARS

Introduction

About the Practice Tests for reading

The tests are intended for use during the spring and summer terms of Year 6 in preparation for the National Tests. They are written to cover the content domain of the *Key Stage 2 English reading test framework for the National Curriculum tests from 2016* (Standards & Testing Agency, 2015). The tests **as a whole** provide complete coverage of the content domain.

There are three tests in total and each test contains three texts, covering a balance of fiction, non-fiction and poetry. Test demand increases within each test, as in the National Test, so initial questions are generally easier than those towards the end of each test, allowing for the chronology to remain correct.

To reduce the amount of referring back and forth between answer sections and texts, we have located the questions after each text rather than at the end of the test. To minimise this further, you may choose to collate your photocopied pages into a texts booklet and an answer booklet.

How to use the Practice Tests

Preparation and timings

1. Help your child prepare for each paper by simulating test conditions.
2. Ensure your child is seated appropriately in front of the paper they are going to work on.
3. Your child will need pens or pencils, and erasers.
4. There are no time limits for the tests but normal practice is to allow a minute per mark for written tests. Help with reading may be given using the same rules as when providing a reader with the Key Stage 2 tests.

Supporting children during the tests

Before the test explain to your child that the test is an opportunity to show what they know, understand and can do. They should try to answer all the questions but should not worry if there are some they can't do.

Many children will be able to work independently in the tests, with minimal support. However, children should be encouraged to 'have a go' at a question, or to move on to a fresh question if they appear to be stuck. Return to difficult questions if you have enough time at the end.

It is important that children receive appropriate support, but are not unfairly advantaged or disadvantaged. Throughout the tests, therefore, you may read, explain or sign to a child any parts of the test that include instructions, for example by demonstrating how to fill in a table.

Marking the tests

Use the mark scheme and your own judgement to award marks. Do not award half marks. Note that a number of questions in each test may require children to do more than one thing for one mark. The mark scheme provides clear guidance in the allocation of marks to support consistent marking of the tests.

It is useful for your child to mark their own test questions from time to time. Your child can look at the test sheets and mark them as you read out the question and answer. You will need to check that your child is marking accurately. This approach also provides an opportunity to recap on any questions that your child found difficult to answer.

Keep track of your child's score using the table on the inside back cover of this book.

Test 1

The story of the Minotaur

King Minos of Crete was a powerful man, feared by the rulers of the lands around him. But his demands on Athens became too much for them to bear.

King Minos had a great palace built for himself. Inside this palace, Minos had built a giant maze, a labyrinth, and at the centre of the maze he kept a terrifying creature, the Minotaur. Now this was no ordinary animal; it was a monster, half man and half bull.

It was powerful and savage and it loved to eat the flesh of the humans who had been shut into the labyrinth by King Minos.

As for Athens, Minos demanded that every year the king send him seven young men and seven young women.

'Why do we send these young people to Crete every year?' Theseus asked his father, the King of Athens. 'And why is it that none of them ever return?'

'Because if we did not send them, Minos would wage war on us and it is a war that we would not win,' said King Aegeus. 'And they do not return because they do not go to Crete as slaves. They go as food for the Minotaur.'

'Father, this is terrible,' shouted Theseus, 'we cannot let this go on. We cannot sacrifice any more of our young citizens to this tyrant. When it is time to send the next tribute, I will go as one of them and I vow that it is the last time the Minotaur will be fed with the flesh of any of our people.'

'Then I wish you good luck, my son,' cried his father, 'I shall keep watch for you every day. If you are successful, take down these black sails and replace them with white ones. That way, I will know you are coming home safe to me.'

As the ship docked in Crete, King Minos himself came down to inspect the prisoners from Athens.

Theseus stepped forward. 'I will go first. I am Theseus, Prince of Athens, and I do not fear what is within the walls of your maze.'

Standing behind the king, listening, was his daughter, Ariadne. From the moment she set eyes on Theseus, Ariadne fell in love with him and decided that she would help him.

'Theseus, take this,' she whispered. She threw him a great ball of string and he tied one end of it to the entrance. He smiled at her, turned and began to make his way into the maze, the string playing out behind him as he went.

Turning a corner, with his hands held out in front of him feeling his way, Theseus suddenly touched what felt like a huge bony horn.

He was picked up between the Minotaur's horns and tossed high into the air. When he landed on the hard cold stone, he felt the animal's huge hooves come down on his chest.

But Theseus was no ordinary man. He was the son of the king, he was brave and he was stubborn.

He grabbed the animal's huge horns, and kept on twisting the great head from side to side. The creature's neck snapped, it gurgled its last breath and fell to the floor with an enormous thud.

As Theseus neared the entrance of the labyrinth, the darkness began to fade and he made out the figure of Ariadne, waiting for his return.

'You must take me back to Athens with you,' she cried. 'My father will kill me when he finds out that I have helped you.'

Quickly and quietly, they unfurled the great black sails of their ship and headed for home.

'I cannot believe how my life has changed,' said Ariadne, as they sailed across the calm seas towards Athens. 'To think that I am free of my cruel father and that I will soon be married to a great prince.'

'Married?' said Theseus. 'Oh, yes, that will be ... er ... wonderful.' But in truth, Theseus did not really find her attractive.

So, when their ship docked at an island on their way home to collect fresh water, Theseus sent Ariadne off to find bread and fruit. The moment she was gone, he set sail and left her on the island. Now, you might think that this was a bad way to reward someone who had helped him and had saved him from certain death.

The gods clearly thought the same thing, for they had a further horror in store for him, as a punishment for his ungrateful treatment of the young girl.

In his haste to get away, Theseus forgot to change his sails to white. King Aegeus, waiting on the headland, saw the ship approaching with its black sails flying in the wind. 'My son has failed and he is dead,' he cried. And in despair, he flung himself from the cliff into the raging waters below.

Name:	Class:	Date:	Total marks: /50

1 *Inside this palace, Minos had built a giant maze, a labyrinth, and at the centre of the maze he kept a* ***terrifying*** *creature.*

1 mark

Which word is closest in meaning to *terrifying*?

Tick **one**.

mighty ☐

petrifying ☐

amazing ☐

powerful ☐

2 The story explains that King Minos demanded that people from Athens be sent to him to feed the Minotaur.

2 marks

What does this tell you about the character of King Minos?

Give **two** features of his character.

1. ______________________________

2. ______________________________

3 *It was powerful and savage and it loved to eat the flesh of the humans who had been shut into the labyrinth by King Minos.*

1 mark

What is this a description of?

____

/4

Total for this page

4 Look at what Theseus says to his father in the paragraph beginning: *'Father, this is terrible ...'*

What is the **main** reason for his decision to go to Crete?

____

____

1 mark

5 *'We cannot sacrifice any more of our young citizens to this **tyrant**.'*

Why was *tyrant* an appropriate word to describe King Minos?

Tick **one**.

He was unfriendly. ☐

He was serious. ☐

He was cruel. ☐

He was caring. ☐

1 mark

6 How does the final paragraph link back to the paragraph beginning: *'Then I wish you good luck, my son,' cried his father?*

____

____

____

2 marks

/4

Total for this page

7 What did King Aegeus tell Theseus to do to signal Theseus's safe return?

____

1 mark

8 Look at the paragraph beginning: *Standing behind the king …*

Why did Ariadne insist that Theseus should take her back to Athens with him?

____

____

1 mark

9 Look at the paragraph beginning: *'You must take me back to Athens …,'* to the end of the story.

Give **two** things that Ariadne did that show she did not agree with her father.

1. ____

2. ____

2 marks

10 What do you think Ariadne did when she found out Theseus had sailed away without her?

____

____

1 mark

/5

Total for this page

11 Look at the paragraph beginning: *The gods clearly thought the same thing ...*

Find and **copy** the word which means that the gods were about to give Theseus a shock.

____

1 mark

12 How do you think Aegeus felt when he saw the sails were black?

Give **one** feeling, using evidence from the text to support your answer.

Feeling ______________________________

Evidence ______________________________

____

____

2 marks

13 Number the following events 1–5 to show the order in which they happened.

The first one has been done for you.

At the centre of the maze was the Minotaur.	☐
Theseus is picked up by the Minotaur.	☐
King Minos builds a giant maze.	1
Aegeus presumes that Theseus has died.	☐
Theseus and Ariadne sail across the calm seas.	☐

1 mark

/4

Total for this page

Things that go BUMP in the night!

Contents

Do you believe in ghosts?

Ghosts. What do you really think about them? Is it true that most of us love a good scary ghost story? Children and adults alike wonder about the existence of ghosts. Some reject the notion. Others insist that ghosts exist and tell of experiences – their own or friend-of-a-friend stories – as proof.

What is a ghost?

Although definitions vary, the most common one is that ghosts are spirits of dead people that linger on Earth. According to tradition, ghosts are invisible but can permit humans to see them.

Of course, either a thing exists or it doesn't. No amount of belief will cause ghosts to exist if they don't; nor could personal opinion cause ghosts not to exist if, in fact, they truly do exist.

Ghosts at royal residences

Where better to kick things off than the Queen's official workplace and London residence, Buckingham Palace.

It is said that the rear terrace of Buckingham Palace is haunted by the ghost of an enchained monk in a brown cowl. He is believed to be the spirit of a monk who died in a punishment cell from a time when a monastery stood on the site.

Another ghost that has been reported is that of Major John Gwynne, who served as King Edward VII's private secretary. After his divorce from his wife, the Major was shunned by upper society. Unable to cope with a life of shame, he died in his first floor office.

Royal ghosts – at what cost?

Windsor Castle is perhaps the most haunted of all the royal residences, with as many as 25 ghosts reported. The ghost of Elizabeth I has been seen by several members of the royal family, including Queen Elizabeth II and her sister Margaret. Often seen in the library, her footsteps can be heard on the bare floorboards, before her striking presence appears.

The ghost of George III has been witnessed, looking longingly out of the room beneath the library, where he was confined during his several periods of madness.

Henry VIII is said to haunt the deanery cloisters, often heard hobbling around, the sound of his ulcerated leg thudding on the floor as he walks.

One of the most notorious ghosts of Balmoral Castle is that of John Brown. Servant to Queen Victoria, they apparently fell in love; however, this remains a matter of conjecture. His ghost is often seen walking the corridors, usually wearing a kilt. Queen Elizabeth II has also reported the feeling of his presence throughout the castle.

Of course, ghostly experiences at royal residences are great news for conservationists, who often struggle to meet the rising costs of maintaining these rather grand buildings. Tourist tickets are a major contributor in developing the funds necessary to preserve the buildings and their contents. In return, tourists are treated to British history at first hand, and if they are really lucky, a ghostly sighting! However, the increase in tourist activity can have a potentially damaging effect on our living history. It has been said that many objects have been worn out and even stolen occasionally. Car parks have had to be created and the grounds maintained to accommodate vast numbers of vehicles. Littering, though not a major concern at the moment, has also contributed to an increase in maintenance costs. Despite the fact that tickets are arguably expensive, thousands of tourists still flock to the royal palaces every year.

14 Look at the section headed: ***Do you believe in ghosts?***

What would be a suitable replacement for this sub-heading?

1 mark

Tick **one**.

Do children believe in ghosts? ☐

Do you think ghosts exist? ☐

Do adults believe ghosts exist? ☐

Are ghost stories real? ☐

15 Who wonders about the existence of ghosts?

Give **two** different examples.

1 mark

1. ______________________________

2. ______________________________

16 Look at the section headed: ***Do you believe in ghosts?***

Find and **copy one** word that is closest in meaning to *a thought*.

1 mark

____

/3

Total for this page

17 Look at the section headed: ***What is a ghost?***

Can ghosts be seen by everyone?

Find and **copy one** line from the text that explains this.

____

____

1 mark

18 a) The main idea in the section headed ***Ghosts at royal residences*** is that Buckingham Palace is …

Tick **one**.

not haunted. ☐

the home of the Queen. ☐

haunted. ☐

the home of John Gwynne. ☐

1 mark

b) Give **one** detail to support this idea.

____

1 mark

19 Look at the paragraph beginning: *Windsor Castle is perhaps the most haunted …*

Find and **copy one** word that is closest in meaning to *a person's home.*

____

1 mark

/4

Total for this page

20 Who has been viewed by several members of the royal family?

1 mark

21 *The ghost of George III has been witnessed, looking longingly out of the room beneath the library …*

What does the word *longingly* tell you about how he felt?

1 mark

22 Look at the paragraph beginning: *One of the most notorious ghosts of Balmoral Castle …*

Find and **copy one** word that suggests that the idea that Queen Victoria and John Brown fell in love may **not** be true.

1 mark

23 Which ghost wears a kilt?

1 mark

/4

Total for this page

24 Match each ghost to the place in which it has been sighted.

One has been done for you.

Ghost	Place
George III	corridors
a monk	library
Henry VIII	rear terrace
John Brown	room beneath the library
Elizabeth I	cloisters

2 marks

25 Look at the section headed: ***Royal ghosts – at what cost?***

Explain **one** positive and **one** negative outcome, using evidence from the text to support your answer.

Positive:

Negative:

3 marks

/5

Total for this page

26 Draw lines to match each section to its main content.

One has been done for you.

1 mark

Section	Content
Contents	highlights the different ghosts that lived in palaces and castles
Do you believe in ghosts?	presents the differing viewpoints on having ghosts
What is a ghost?	introduces the debate about whether or not ghosts exist
Ghosts at royal residences	shows what is inside the book
Royal ghosts – at what cost?	gives information about the description of a ghost

/1

Total for this page

The lion and Albert

There's a famous seaside place called Blackpool,
That's noted for fresh air and fun,
And Mr and Mrs Ramsbottom
Went there with young Albert, their son.

A grand little lad was their Albert,
All dressed in his best; quite a swell
'E'd a stick with an 'orse's 'ead 'andle,
The finest that Woolworth's could sell.

They didn't think much of the ocean:
The waves, they was fiddlin' and small
There was no wrecks and nobody drownded,
Fact, nothing to laugh at at all.

So, seeking for further amusement,
They paid and went into the zoo,
Where they'd lions and tigers and camels,
And old ale and sandwiches too.

There were one great big lion called Wallace;
His nose were all covered with scars –
He lay in a somnolent posture,
With the side of his face to the bars.

Now Albert had heard about lions,
How they were ferocious and wild –
To see Wallace lying so peaceful,
Well, it didn't seem right to the child.

So straightway the brave little feller,
Not showing a morsel of fear,
Took his stick with the 'orse's 'ead 'andle
And pushed it in Wallace's ear.

You could see that the lion didn't like it,
For giving a kind of a roll,
He pulled Albert inside the cage with 'im,
And swallowed the little lad 'ole.

Then Pa, who had seen the occurrence,
And didn't know what to do next,
Said, "Mother! Yon lion's 'et Albert",
And Mother said "Well, I am vexed!"

So Mr and Mrs Ramsbottom –
Quite rightly, when all's said and done –
Complained to the Animal Keeper,
That the lion had eaten their son.

The keeper was quite nice about it ;
He said "What a nasty mishap.
Are you sure that it's your boy he's eaten?"
Pa said "Am I sure? There's his cap!"

The manager had to be sent for.
He came and he said, "What's to do?"
Pa said, "Yon lion's 'et Albert,
And 'im in his Sunday clothes, too."

Then Mother said, "Right's right, young feller;
I think it's a shame and a sin,
For a lion to go and eat Albert,
And after we've paid to come in."

The manager wanted no trouble
He took out his purse right away,
Saying "How much to settle the matter?"
And Pa said "What do you usually pay?"

But Mother had turned a bit awkward
When she thought where her Albert had gone
She said "No! someone's got to be summonsed" –
So that were decided upon.

Round they went to the P'lice Station
In front of the Magistrate chap;
They told 'im what happened to Albert
And proved it by showing his cap.

The Magistrate gave his opinion
That no one was really to blame
And he said that he hoped the Ramsbottoms
Would have further sons to their name.

At that Mother got proper blazing.
"And thank you, sir, kindly," said she
"What waste all our lives raising children
To feed ruddy lions? Not me!"

27 Look at the first verse.

Find and **copy one** word that is closest in meaning to *well known*.

____

1 mark

28 **Find** and **copy** a line from the poem that shows it is written in dialect.

____

1 mark

29 Look at the third and fourth verses.

Write the main idea of these verses in **one** sentence.

____

1 mark

30 What animals were at the zoo?

Give **two** different animals.

1. ______________________________

2. ______________________________

1 mark

/4

Total for this page

31 Why did Albert decide to provoke the lion?

1 mark

32 *So straightway the brave little feller*

Not showing a morsel of fear

Why has the word *morsel* been used to describe the boy's fear?

1 mark

33 What did Albert do to show that he was not afraid of the lion?

1 mark

/3

Total for this page

34 Look at the verses beginning: *Now Albert had heard about lions …* and: *So straightway the brave little feller …*

3 marks

What do these verses tell you about Albert's character?

Explain **two** features of his character, using evidence from the text to support your answer.

1. ______________________________

____

____

2. ______________________________

____

____

35 Look at the verse beginning: *So the manager had to be sent for …* and ending: *And 'im in his Sunday clothes, too."*

1 mark

What does *Sunday clothes* mean?

____

____

/4

Total for this page

36 Look at the verse beginning: *Then Mother said, "Right's right, young feller ...*

2 marks

How is Mother feeling?

Explain **one** feeling, using evidence from the text to support your answer.

Feeling ______________________________

Evidence ______________________________

____

____

37 The poem suggests that ...

1 mark

Tick **one**.

life is great. ☐

family days out are fun. ☐

life is unpredictable. ☐

family is important. ☐

/3

Total for this page

38 What is the purpose of this poem?

1 mark

Tick **one**.

to entertain ☐

to scare ☐

to inform ☐

to tempt ☐

39 Mother's opinion towards saving Albert changes by the end of the poem.

Explain this change.

1 mark

____

____

/2

Total for this page

Test 2

Lighthouse history

Why were lighthouses built?

Lighthouses were constructed to mark the major headlands and sandbanks. On a smaller scale, lights were also erected at the entrances to ports, harbours and rivers.

The first lights

Trading by sea has been a principal activity of all civilisations. However, moving goods and cargoes by water involves facing difficulties and dangers such as storms and bad weather, avoiding reefs, **headlands**, sandbanks and cliffs, and making safe passage into ports and harbours.

The earliest aids to navigation were beacons or **daymarks**, sited near harbours or ports rather than on headlands or reefs, to help ships reach their destinations safely. The earliest lighthouses were in the Mediterranean, and the oldest such structure of which written records survive was that on the island of Pharos, off Alexandria, on the northern coast of Egypt.

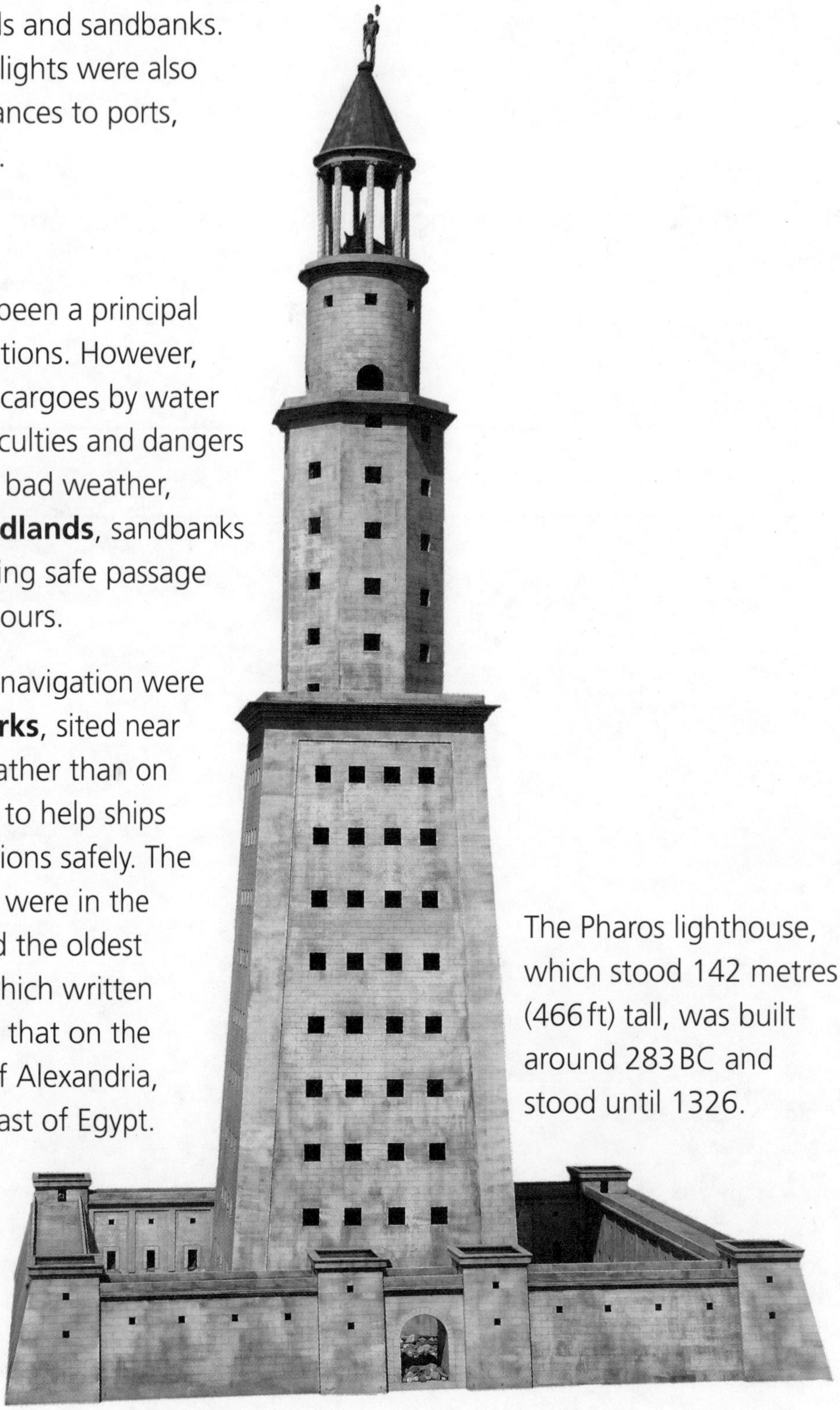

The Pharos lighthouse, which stood 142 metres (466 ft) tall, was built around 283 BC and stood until 1326.

Coal and lighthouses

The development of lighthouses around the coasts of the British Isles reflected **trade routes**. The earliest British lights were built on the south and east coasts to assist vessels trading with European ports. But by the 17th century, lights along the east coast helped to guide **colliers** carrying coal from the ports of the north-east to London.

The coal trade from Newcastle and Sunderland to London dominated coastal traffic. Just less than 50% of coastal shipping in the period 1779 to 1884 was devoted to coal carriage. Indeed, the coal trade was the largest single activity of coastal shipping during the industrial revolution.

Roker Pier Lighthouse, Sunderland
Built: 1903
Tower: 75 ft
Colour: red and white naturally coloured stone
Material: natural stone and granite
Builder: Henry Hay Wake

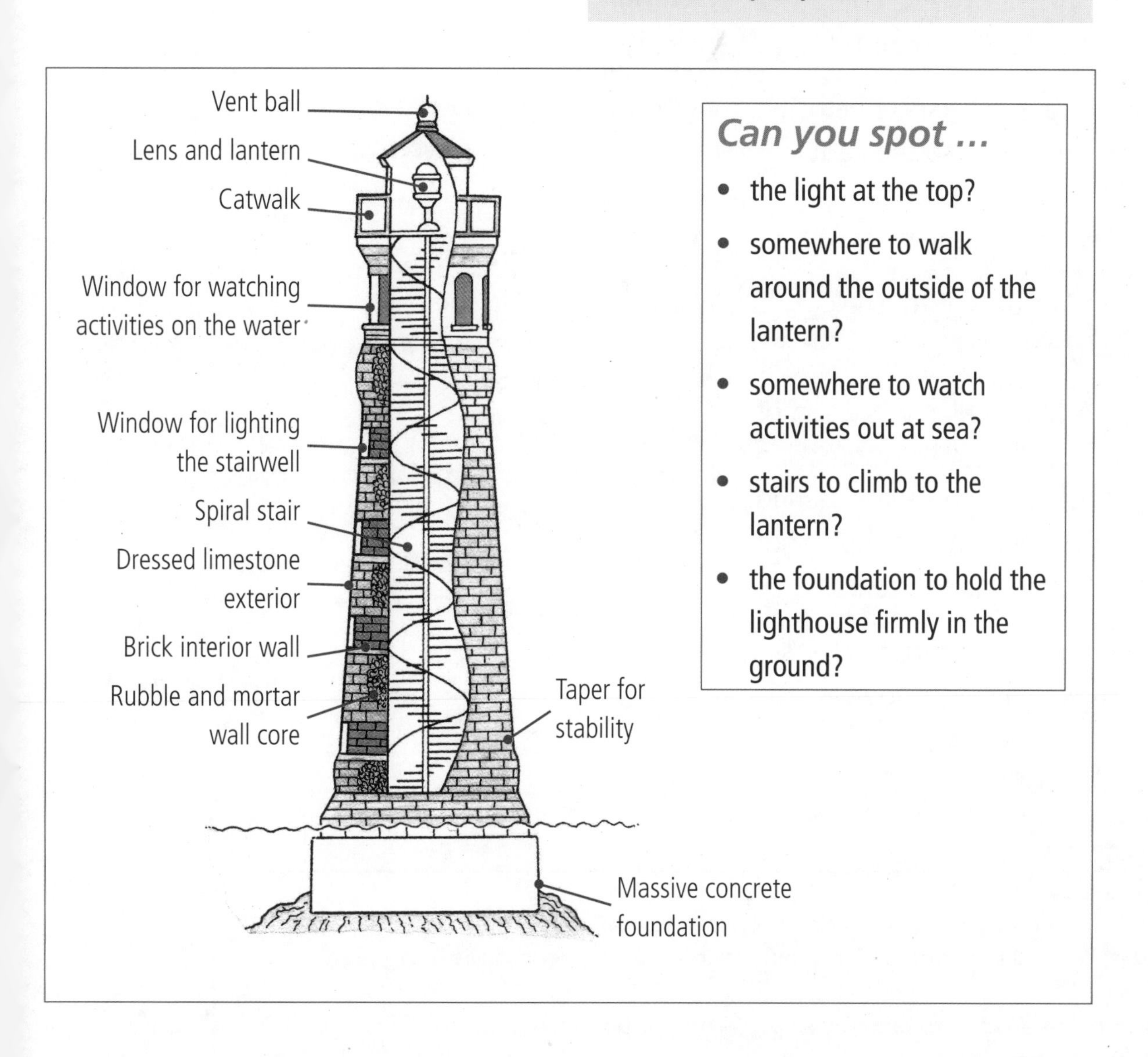

Author interview: *The Lighthouse Keeper's Lunch*

Ronda Armitage is the author of a very famous children's book series about a lighthouse keeper called Mr Grinling.

Where do you get your ideas from?

The idea for *The Lighthouse Keeper's Lunch* came from a question our son asked many years ago. My husband David and I had taken our children down to look at a lighthouse near us. We were standing on the cliffs when my son noticed a wire running from the cliff down to the lighthouse.

'What's that wire for?' he asked.

It was probably a wire taking electricity down to the lighthouse so the light would shine brightly out to sea every night, but David didn't say that.

'I expect that's for the lighthouse keeper's lunch,' David said.

DAVID TOLD A LIE!! Well, it was a sort of a lie but you could also say he was making up a story. Now that day I was wearing my best listening ears. I'm sure you've got some too. I was listening for stories.

'What a good idea,' I thought. 'That's what I could write a story about: a lighthouse keeper who gets his lunch in a basket down a wire.'

Victorian fact

A very famous story tells of a young, Victorian lighthouse keeper's daughter, called Grace Darling, who was born in 1815 in Bamburgh, Northumberland.

She is famous for helping her father, William Darling, in the rescue of survivors from the shipwrecked *Forfarshire* in 1838. Grace spotted the shipwreck of the *Forfarshire* from the windows of their home, in Longstone lighthouse, and is famous for participating in the rescue of survivors. She died aged only 26.

Glossary

- **headland** a narrow piece of land that projects from a coastline into the sea
- **daymark** a tall structure on land, only visible by day, which aids navigation by sailors
- **trade route** any route taken by ships carrying goods
- **collier** ship carrying coal

Name:	Class:	Date:	Total marks: /50

1 According to the text, why were lighthouses built?

Give **two** reasons from the text.

1. ______________________________

2. ______________________________

2 marks

2 Look at the section headed: ***The first lights***.

What difficulties are faced when moving goods and cargoes by water?

Give **three** difficulties.

1. ____________________

2. ____________________

3. ____________________

3 marks

3 Why were beacons or daymarks sited near harbours or ports?

____

____

1 mark

/6

Total for this page

4 Look at the section headed: ***Coal and lighthouses.***

Find and **copy two** facts about coal.

1. ______________________

2. ______________________

2 marks

5 *The coal trade from Newcastle and Sunderland to London dominated coastal traffic.*

What does the word *dominated* mean in this sentence?

____

____

1 mark

6 Look at the paragraph beginning: *The coal trade from Newcastle and Sunderland …*

How do we know that the coal trade was the biggest activity?

____

____

1 mark

/4

Total for this page

7 How tall is the Roker Pier Lighthouse?

____

1 mark

8 What is the purpose of the ***Can you spot …*** text box?

1 mark

Tick **two**.

to keep the reader engaged with the text ☐

to provide extra information ☐

to encourage the reader to look for technical information ☐

to show how the lighthouse works ☐

9 Look at the section headed: ***Where do you get your ideas from?***

Explain how David's lie inspired Ronda Armitage to write her book.

1 mark

____

____

/3

Total for this page

10 Look at the section headed: ***Victorian fact***.

Write a suitable heading to replace *Victorian fact*.

____

1 mark

11 Why is Grace Darling famous?

____

____

1 mark

12 Match each event to the date it happened.

Event	Date
The Pharos lighthouse was built.	1815
Grace Darling was born.	1838
The Forfarshire was shipwrecked.	1903
Roker Pier lighthouse was built.	283 BC

2 marks

/4

Total for this page

13 Using the information from the text, put a tick in the correct box to show whether each statement is **true** or **false**.

2 mark

One has been done for you.

	True	False
The Pharos lighthouse was 200 metres tall.		
Almost 100% of coastal shipping in the period 1779 to 1884 was devoted to coal carriage.		
The lighthouse was tapered for stability.	✔	
Grace Darling died aged 26.		

14 What is the purpose of this text?

1 mark

Tick **one**.

to entertain ☐

to persuade ☐

to inform ☐

to recount ☐

/3

Total for this page

The hollow land

I'm Bell Teesdale. I'm a lad. I'm eight.

All down this dale where I live there's dozens of little houses with grass growing between the stones and for years there's been none of them wanted. They're too old or too far out or that bit too high for farmers now. There was miners once – it's what's called the hollow land – but they're here no more. So the little houses is all **forsook**. They have big **garths** round them, and pasture for grass-letting – sheep and that – and grand hay fields. Maybe just too many buttercups blowing silver in June, but grand hay for all that, given a fair week or two after dipping time.

All these little farm houses for years stood empty, all the old farming families gone and the roofs falling in and the swallows and swifts swooping into bedrooms and muck trailing down inside the stone walls. So incomers come. They buy these little houses when they can, or they rent or lease them. Manchester folks or even London folks, with big estate cars full of packet food you don't see round here, and great soft dogs that's never seen another animal.

All down Mallerstang there's **becks** running down off the **fell**. It's **bonny**. Down off the sharp **scales**, dry in summer till one single drop of rain sends them running and rushing and tumbling down the fell-side like threads of silk. Like cob-webs. And when the wind blow across the dale these becks gasp, and they rise up on themselves like the wild horses in Wateryate Bottom. They rise up on their hind legs. Or like smoke blowing, like ever so many bonfires, not water at all, all smoking in the wind between Castledale and the Moorcock toward Wensleydale. It's bonny.

And townsfolk come looking at all this now where once they only went to the Lake District over the west. Renting and leasing they come. Talking south. 'Why'd they come?' I ask our grandad who's leased the farm house he used to live in (my gran died). 'There's not owt for 'em here. What's use of a farm to them? Just for sitting in. Never a thing going on.'

'Resting,' says my grandad. 'They take 'em for resting in after London.'

Well, this family that come to my grandad's old house, Light Trees, wasn't resting. Not resting at all. There's a mother and a father and four or five great lads, some of them friends only, and there's a little lad, Harry, and the racket they make can be heard as far as Garsdale likely.

They has the house – our gran and grandad's old house see – but we still keep all the farm buildings and work them and we've right to the hay off the Home Field.

There's good cow **byres**, dipping pens, **bull's hull** and clipping shed. So we're clipping and dipping and drenching and putting the cows to the bull regardless. Sometimes there's a hundred sheep solid across our yard so they can't get their car over to the yard gate. But it was in the arrangement, mind. My dad always says, 'We're about to bring in sheep, Mr Bateman' – it's what they're called, Bateman – 'We're bringing in sheep. Would you like to get your car out first? We'll hold things back.' There's maybe four, five and six of our sheep-dogs lying watching, and their soft dog lying watching our dogs, but never going near.

Then from out the house comes their music playing, and lads yelling and laughing and a radio or two going and the London mother cooking these Italian-style suppers and their telephone ringing (they've got in the telephone like they've got in a fridge) and they're all saying, this London lot, '*Beautiful* evening Mr Teesdale' – my dad – 'And what are you doing with the sheep tonight? You're giving us quite an *education*.'

And there's this little lad, Harry, just stands there not saying owt.

Now there's one night, the first night of hay-time, and we're all **slathered out**, even my dad. It's perfect. A right hot summer and a right hot night and a bright moon. Yesterday my dad said, 'Tomorrow we'll mow hay. We'll mow all day and if need be through the night. There may be rain by Sunday.'

He's never wrong, my dad, so we – my mum and our Eileen and our Eileen's boyfriend and Grandad and all of us – we set up and we finish the High Field and Miner's Acre by tea-time. And then we sets to with the Home Field – that's the great big good field round Light Trees. Light Trees stand right in it.

It makes a rare clatter our tractor and cutter, louder than their **transistors** – clatter, clatter, clatter, round and round and round – and after a bit, well maybe two hours, their heads beginning to bob from windows. Then round ten-eleven o'clock and the summer light starts fading and it's still clatter, clatter, there's electric lights flashing on and off inside Light Trees and this London father comes out.

Glossary

- **forsook** abandoned
- **garths** large open spaces
- **becks** streams
- **fell** mountain
- **bonny** pretty
- **scales** slopes
- **byres** cowsheds
- **bull's hull** outbuilding for holding bulls
- **slathered out** exhausted
- **transistors** radios

15 Look at the paragraph beginning: *All down this dale where I live …*

Why do you think this area of land in the Dales is known as *the hollow land*?

____

____

2 marks

16 The text suggests that the fields that need mowing are very large.

Give **two** details to support this idea.

1. ____

2. ____

2 marks

17 Look at the paragraph beginning: *All these little farm houses …*

What **two differences** does the text suggest about people from Manchester and London, and people from the Dales?

1. ____

2. ____

1 mark

/5

Total for this page

18 *... dry in summer till one single drop of rain sends them running and rushing and tumbling down the fell-side like threads of silk. Like cob-webs.*

1 mark

What does the description above suggest about the stream?

Tick **one**.

It is very dry.	☐
It spreads across the hillside.	☐
It is a spiderweb.	☐
It is burning and smoking.	☐

19 Look at the paragraph beginning: *Well, this family that come ...*

1 mark

Find and **copy one** word that is closest in meaning to *making a loud noise.*

____

/2

Total for this page

20 Using the information from page 33, put a tick in the correct box to show whether each statement is **true** or **false**.

2 marks

	True	False
The hollow land used to have miners working there.		
There are lots of farming families living in the hollow land.		
There are wild horses in Wateryate Bottom.		
A big family live in Bell Teesdale's gran and grandad's old house.		

21 The Bateman family is noisy.

Give **two** details to support this.

2 marks

1. ______________________________

2. ______________________________

22 Give **two** details to show how the Batemans are different to the Teesdales.

2 marks

1. ______________________________

2. ______________________________

/6

Total for this page

23 Look at the paragraph beginning: *Now there's one night, ...*

Why were the Teesdale family exhausted?

____

1 mark

24 Look at the paragraph beginning: *It makes a rare clatter our tractor ... clatter, clatter, clatter*

What does the description above tell you about the tractor?

____

1 mark

25 *... their heads beginning to bob from windows.*

Who is this description about?

____

1 mark

26 Look at the last sentence of the final paragraph.

What might the London father do when he comes out of the house?

Explain fully, using evidence from the text to support your answer.

____

____

____

2 marks

/5

Total for this page

The Lady of Shalott

Part I

On either side the river lie
Long fields of barley and of rye,
That clothe the **wold** and meet the sky;
And thro' the field the road runs by
    To many-tower'd Camelot;
The yellow-leaved waterlily
The green-sheathed daffodilly
Tremble in the water chilly
    Round about Shalott.

Willows whiten, aspens shiver.
The sunbeam showers break and quiver
In the stream that runneth ever
By the island in the river
    Flowing down to Camelot.
Four grey walls, and four grey towers
Overlook a space of flowers,
And the silent isle **imbowers**
    The Lady of Shalott.

Underneath the bearded barley,
The **reaper**, reaping late and early,
Hears her ever chanting cheerly,
Like an angel, singing clearly,
    O'er the stream of Camelot.
Piling the sheaves in furrows airy,
Beneath the moon, the reaper weary
Listening whispers, 'Tis the fairy,
    Lady of Shalott.'

The little isle is all **inrail'd**
With a rose-fence, and **overtrail'd**
With roses: by the marge **unhail'd**
The **shallop** flitteth silken sail'd,
    Skimming down to Camelot.
A pearl garland winds her head:
She leaneth on a velvet bed,
Full royally **apparelled**,
    The Lady of Shalott.

Glossary

- **wold** countryside
- **imbowers** shelters
- **reaper** farmer
- **inrail'd** enclosed
- **overtrail'd** overgrown
- **unhail'd** unnoticed
- **shallop** boat
- **apparelled** clothed

Part II

No time hath she to sport and play:
A charmed web she weaves away.
A curse is on her, if she stay
Her weaving, either night or day,
    To look down to Camelot.
She knows not what the curse may be;
Therefore she weaveth steadily,
Therefore no other care hath she,
    The Lady of Shalott.

She lives with little joy or fear.
Over the water, running near,
The sheepbell tinkles in her ear.
Before her hangs a mirror clear,
    Reflecting tower'd Camelot.
And as the mazy web she whirls,
She sees the surly village **churls**,
And the red cloaks of market girls
    Pass onward from Shalott.

Sometimes a troop of damsels glad,
An abbot on an ambling **pad**,
Sometimes a curly shepherd lad,
Or long-hair'd page in crimson clad,
    Goes by to tower'd Camelot:
And sometimes thro' the mirror blue
The knights come riding two and two:
She hath no loyal knight and true,
    The Lady of Shalott.

But in her web she still delights
To weave the mirror's magic sights,
For often thro' the silent nights
A funeral, with plumes and lights
    And music, came from Camelot:
Or when the moon was overhead
Came two young lovers lately wed;
'I am half sick of shadows,' said
    The Lady of Shalott.

Glossary

- **churls** villagers
- **pad** road

27 Look at the first verse.

Long fields of barley and of rye,

That clothe the wold [countryside] *and meet the sky; …*

What does this description tell you about the countryside?

1 mark

28 *The green-sheathed daffodilly*

Tremble in the water chilly

Why is *tremble* a suitable word to describe the daffodils?

1 mark

29 *Like an angel, singing clearly …*

What impression do you get from this description of the Lady of Shalott?

1 mark

/3

Total for this page

30 How do the people of Camelot know the lady is in the tower?

1 mark

31 Look at Part I.

How can you tell that the Lady of Shalott is royal?

Give **two** different ways.

1.

2.

1 mark

32 Look at Part II: *A curse is on her, if she stay …*

What curse has been placed on this lady?

1 mark

33 The lady weaves the things she sees in her mirror.

Find and **copy one** quote to support this idea.

1 mark

/4

Total for this page

34 What impression do you get of the Lady of Shalott's feelings?

Give **two** impressions, using evidence from the text to support your answer.

3 marks

Impression	Evidence

35 Look at Part II: *But in her web she still delights ...*

What is her web?

1 mark

36 The main ideas of the poem are that the Lady of Shalott ...

Tick **two**.

- is inside a tower. ☐
- is looking at a tower. ☐
- lives in Camelot. ☐
- is under a curse. ☐

1 mark

/5

Total for this page

Test 3

Crystals

Crystals are associated with perfection, transparency and clarity. Many crystals fit these ideals, especially those cut as gemstones, but most are neither perfect nor transparent. Crystals are solid materials in which the atoms are arranged in a regular pattern.

Did you know?

A material can exist as a solid, a liquid or a gas depending on its temperature.

Water is made of atoms of hydrogen and oxygen bound together to form molecules. In its solid form (ice), the water molecules are arranged in a regular order and form a crystalline solid.

A world of crystals

Crystals are all around us. We live on a crystal planet in a crystal world. The rocks which form the Earth, the Moon and meteorites (pieces of rock from space), are made up of minerals and virtually all of these minerals are made up of crystals. Crystalline particles make up mountains and form the ocean floors. When we cross the beach we tread on crystals.

Crystals at home and at work

We use crystals at home and at work; indeed, crystals are vital to today's technology.

Crystals at home

Many everyday objects in the home are crystalline. There are ice crystals in the freezer, salt and sugar crystals in the food cupboard and in food itself. There are silicon crystal chips in the fridge and washing machine. The TV, telephone, radio and camera work because of crystals. The house is built of materials which are mostly crystalline, and outside, bikes and cars stand slowly rusting – crystallising!

Crystals at work

Crystals are used in control circuits, machines, communications and medicine.

> ***Fact***
>
> Diamonds do not corrode. This is one reason why sometimes diamond blades are used in scalpels for surgery.

The colour of crystals

The colour of a crystal can be its most striking feature. The causes of colour are varied and many minerals occur in a range of colours.

For example, quartz, diamond, beryl and corundum can be red, green, yellow and blue.

What is it?

This is the first question to ask about a mineral, crystal or gemstone. Most minerals have a clearly identifiable crystal structure. Colour and surface features can be studied using a hand lens. Other properties, such as 'hardness', can be studied using scientific equipment.

Hardness

The property of hardness is dependent upon the strength of the forces holding atoms together in a solid.

The scale below was devised by F. Mohs in 1812.

Mineral	Talc	Gypsum	Calcite	Fluorite	Apatite
Hardness	1	2	3	4	5

Mineral	Orthoclase	Quartz	Topaz	Corundum	Diamond
Hardness	6	7	8	9	10

Making them sparkle!

Some rough crystals are beautifully shaped and have breathtaking lustre and colour, but most are worn down or have other imperfections. A skilled stone cutter and polisher, called a 'lapidary', can turn these stones into objects of beauty and value by using their individual qualities in the right way.

Name:	Class:	Date:	Total marks: /50

1 Look at the first section.

What are crystals associated with?

Give **three** things.

2 marks

1. ______________________

2. ______________________

3. ______________________

2 Look at the section headed: ***Did you know?***

What is water in its solid state?

____

1 mark

3 Look at the section headed: ***A world of crystals.***

Which of the following would be a suitable replacement for this sub-heading?

1 mark

Tick **one**.

What are crystal pieces called? ☐

What can crystals do? ☐

Where can crystals be found? ☐

Why are crystals found on beaches? ☐

/4

Total for this page

4 Give **two** household machines that contain crystals, according to the text.

2 marks

1. ______________________

2. ______________________

5 How are crystals used in the workplace?

Give **two** uses.

2 marks

1. ______________________

2. ______________________

6 Give **two** ways to explain how diamonds are different compared to other crystals.

2 marks

1. ______________________

2. ______________________

/6

Total for this page

7 Look at the section headed: ***Hardness***.

Who developed the scale used to measure the hardness of crystals?

____

1 mark

8 Number these crystals 1–5 in order of hardness.

Number 1, the hardest crystal, has been done for you.

fluorite	☐
topaz	☐
apatite	☐
gypsum	☐
diamond	1

1 mark

9 *Some rough crystals are beautifully shaped and have breathtaking lustre …*

What does the word *lustre* mean in this sentence?

Tick **one**.

colour	☐
shape	☐
shine	☐
cut	☐

1 mark

/3

Total for this page

10 What is the job of a lapidary?

____

____

1 mark

11 Draw lines to match each section to its main content.

One has been done for you.

Section	Content
Did you know?	explains how rough crystals can be transformed
Crystals at home	gives information about how hard particular minerals are
Fact	highlights how everyday objects are crystalline
Hardness	explains what a material is
Making them sparkle!	gives information about how diamonds do not corrode

2 marks

12 Using information from the text, tick one box in each row to show whether each statement is a **fact** or an **opinion**.

	Fact	Opinion
We live on a crystal planet.		
Water is made from hydrogen and oxygen.		
A crystal's colour can be its most striking feature.		
Some crystals are beautifully shaped.		

2 marks

/5

Total for this page

Macavity, the mystery cat

Macavity's a Mystery Cat: he's called the Hidden Paw –
For he's the master criminal who can defy the Law.
He's the bafflement of Scotland Yard, the Flying Squad's despair:
For when they reach the scene of crime – *Macavity's not there!*

Macavity, Macavity, there's no one like Macavity,
He's broken every human law, he breaks the law of gravity.
His powers of levitation would make a **fakir** stare,
And when you reach the scene of crime – *Macavity's not there!*
You may seek him in the basement, you may look up in the air –
But I tell you once and once again, *Macavity's not there!*

Macavity's a ginger cat, he's very tall and thin;
You would know him if you saw him, for his eyes are sunken in.
His brow is deeply lined with thought, his head is highly domed;
His coat is dusty from neglect, his whiskers are uncombed.
He sways his head from side to side, with movements like a snake;
And when you think he's half asleep, he's always wide awake.

Macavity, Macavity, there's no one like Macavity,
For he's a fiend in feline shape, a monster of depravity.
You may meet him in a by-street, you may see him in the square –
But when a crime's discovered, then *Macavity's not there!*

He's outwardly respectable. (They say he cheats at cards.)
And his footprints are not found in any file of Scotland Yard's.
And when the larder's looted, or the jewel-case is rifled,
Or when the milk is missing, or another Peke's been stifled,
Or the greenhouse glass is broken, and the trellis past repair –
Ay, there's the wonder of the thing! *Macavity's not there!*

And when the Foreign Office find a Treaty's gone astray,
Or the Admiralty lose some plans and drawings by the way,
There may be a scrap of paper in the hall or on the stair –
But it's useless to investigate – *Macavity's not there!*
And when the loss has been disclosed, the Secret Service say:
'It *must* have been Macavity!' – but he's a mile away.
You'll be sure to find him resting, or a-licking of his thumbs,
Or engaged in doing complicated long division sums.

Glossary

- **fakir** a Muslim or Hindu holy man who appeared to have magic powers

13 Look at the first paragraph.

Macavity is described as the *master criminal.*

What does this description suggest about Macavity?

Explain **both** words.

2 marks

14 Look at the first paragraph.

Find and **copy one** word that means the same as *confusion.*

1 mark

15 Why do you think Macavity never gets caught?

2 marks

16 *His powers of levitation would make a fakir stare, …*

What does this sentence tell you about Macavity's physical abilities?

1 mark

/6

Total for this page

17 Macavity is not very clean.

Give **two different** pieces of evidence from the text to support this.

2 marks

1. ______________________________

2. ______________________________

18 What does the text compare the way Macavity moves his head to?

1 mark

Tick **one**.

a chicken ☐

a snake ☐

a goat ☐

an elephant ☐

19 Look at the fourth verse.

1 mark

... a fiend in a feline shape ...

What does the word *fiend* suggest about Macavity?

____

/4

Total for this page

20 Look at the sixth verse.

Find and **copy** a group of words that shows the Secret Service knows who is responsible for the missing things.

____

1 mark

21 In what ways is Macavity's behaviour extraordinary?

Give **two** ways.

1. ______________________________

2. ______________________________

2 marks

22 According to what you have read, which description best matches the character of Macavity?

Tick **one**.

brave and friendly ☐

magical and vain ☐

violent and shy ☐

clever and thoughtful ☐

1 mark

/4

Total for this page

The travels of Marianne North

Marianne North was an accomplished painter, knowledgeable botanist, enthusiastic traveller and prolific diarist.

She was a remarkable Victorian artist who travelled around the world to satisfy her passion for painting plants. At a time when women rarely travelled alone, many of Marianne's expeditions to remote areas of the globe were fraught with danger, but also with adventure and opportunity.

Algerian stamp showing Marianne North

The life of Marianne North

Marianne North was born in Hastings, Sussex, in 1830. She spent much of her youth travelling in England and Europe, and although she took a sketchbook, as was customary for young Victorian women travellers, music was her mania.

When Marianne was 24, her mother died and when her father died in 1869, Marianne was at last free to visit the tropics. She once wrote that she was 'a very wild bird' and liked 'liberty'. At the age of 40 she began her astonishing series of trips around the world.

Between 1871 and 1885, she visited 16 different countries. Her aim was to paint plants in their habitats and to educate people on the sources of certain products.

Marianne North was a prolific diarist, recording many descriptive and creative accounts of her travels. Read some of her adventures on the next page.

Did you know?

Royal connections Marianne received some tuition from a famous Dutch flower artist and from Valentine Bartholomew, flower painter to Queen Victoria.

Brazil 1872

I started in the *Neva* Royal Mail ship on August 9, 1872. I had a most comfortable cabin, quite a little room, with a square window, and the voyage was most enjoyable. Lisbon was our first halt, which we reached on August 13 at sunset; the entrance to the harbour is striking, with the semi-**Moorish** tower and convent of Bela in the foreground.

Brazil 1872–1883

Of course my first work was to attempt to make a sketch of the great avenue of royal palms (Roystonea regia), which has been so often described.

There was a coarse marigold-looking bloom with the sweetest scent of vanilla, and a large purple-bell begonia creeper with the strongest smell of garlic. A lovely velvet-leaved ipomoea, with large white blossom and dark eye, and a perfectly exquisite rose-coloured begonia bush were very common.

South Africa 1882–1883

While painting the protea flower, I saw the stamens begin to dance, and out came a big green beetle.

Did you know?

Marianne North travelled on many different means of transport which included:

Riding on the back of a mule, travelling in a **jampany**, riding in a mule-drawn cart, travelling on a steamship, riding on horseback, riding in a train, being carried in a **jinricksha** and a **palki**!

Marianne North Gallery at Kew Gardens

Marianne North's paintings can be seen in the Marianne North Gallery at the Royal Botanic Gardens, Kew, designed by her friend James Fergusson. The gallery includes coloured oil paintings of plants, landscapes, birds and animals and includes over 800 paintings.

Did you know?

Marianne North completed over 800 paintings in less than 14 years!

Women artists

Marianne was a great supporter of women. She was particularly keen to promote the work of other women artists (although she was often irritated by certain young ladies who made stupid remarks about her paintings).

In 1884, at the end of her trip to the Seychelles, Marianne's health began to break down. She returned to England, but after a brief rest she decided to visit Chile. She was determined to paint the intriguing Monkey Puzzle trees she knew she would find there. After a stop in Jamaica, she returned from this, her final voyage, in 1885.

Marianne continued arranging the paintings in her gallery and finally retired to a house in Gloucestershire where she made a wonderful garden. Marianne North died on August 30, 1890 at the age of only 59.

Fact

Marianne North met Charles Darwin who told her to 'investigate the flora of Australia and New Zealand'. She took this as a 'royal command' and went at once.

Glossary

- **Moorish** built by the Moors, people from North Africa who invaded Spain
- **jampany** a kind of armchair, with a pole on each side, carried by four men
- **jinricksha** Japanese word for rickshaw, a small, two-wheeled, cart-like passenger vehicle with a fold-down top, pulled by one person
- **palki** a Sikh word for a small, raised platform with canopy for a very important person

23 Look at the first paragraph.

Why were many of Marianne's travels *fraught with danger*?

____

1 mark

24 *... although she took a sketchbook, as was customary for young Victorian women travellers, music was her mania.*

What does the word *mania* mean in this sentence?

____

1 mark

25 Why was Marianne determined to go to Chile?

____

1 mark

/3

Total for this page

26 Marianne North *could* have been a botanist (someone who studies the science of plants) as well as a painter.

Explain why this could be a possibility, using evidence from the text.

2 marks

27 Marianne North was a *prolific diarist.*

What does the word *prolific* tell you about Marianne North as a diarist?

1 mark

28 Look at the section headed: ***Brazil 1872–1883***.

What are *Roystonea regia*?

1 mark

/4

Total for this page

29 Look at the section headed: ***Brazil 1872–1883***.

... coarse marigold-looking bloom ...

What does the word *coarse* tell you about the flower?

1 mark

30 What do the types of transport Marianne used tell you about the ways in which she travelled?

Give an example from the text to support your answer.

2 marks

/3

Total for this page

31 Why did Marianne travel around the world when she knew there would be areas that were *fraught with danger*?

3 marks

Explain **two** reasons, using evidence from the text to support your answer.

1. ____

____

____

2. ____

____

____

32 The main idea in this text is that Marianne North …

1 mark

Tick **one**.

was a Victorian woman. ☐

painted thousands of exotic plants. ☐

has a gallery at Kew Gardens. ☐

was a Victorian artist. ☐

/4

Total for this page

33 Look at the section headed: ***Women artists***.

Marianne North has a very determined character.

Explain **two** ways she is determined, using evidence from the text to support your answer.

1. ______________________________

____

____

2. ______________________________

____

____

3 marks

34 Using the whole text, put a tick in the correct box to show whether each statement is **true** or **false**.

1 mark

	True	False
Marianne North's mother and father died at the same time.		
Marianne reached Lisbon on 13th August at sunrise.		
In South Africa Marianne saw stamens dancing.		
Marianne North retired to a house in Gloucestershire.		

/4

Total for this page

Answers

Test 1 Paper 1: Arithmetic

Qu.	Content domain	Requirement	Additional guidance	Mark
1	3C1	1,095		1
2	5C6a	600		1
3	3C2	510		1
4	3F4	$\frac{8}{9}$		1
5	3N2b	525		1
6	3C1	559		1
7	4C6b	572		1
8	4C7	1,820		1
9	5F10	4.6		1
10	4C6a	12		1
11	5C7a	5,396		1
12	4N2b	1,060		1
13	4C2	2,999		1
14	4F10a	440		1
15	5C5d	36		1
16	4F4	$\frac{1}{2}$	Accept equivalent fraction **OR exact** decimal 0.5	1
17	5C6b	1,456		1
18	5C1	44,200		1
19	5F10	3.85		1
20	6C7a	95,376	Award **2 marks** for the correct answer of 95,376. If the answer is incorrect, award **1 mark** for a formal method of long multiplication with no more than **ONE** arithmetic error, e.g. 3 9 7 4 × 2 4 1 5 8 9 6 7 9 4 8 0 9 5 3 7 5 (error) **OR** 3 9 7 4 × 2 4 1 5 8 9 6 6 9 4 8 0 (error) 8 5 3 7 6 Working must be carried through to reach a final answer for the award of **1 mark**. **Do not** award any marks if the error is in the place value, e.g. the omission of the zero when multiplying the tens. 3 9 7 4 × 2 4 1 5 8 9 6 7 9 4 8 (error) 2 3 8 4 4	2

21	6R2	175		1
22	5C7b	797		1
23	6F9b	12.25		1
24	6F4	$4\frac{7}{10}$		1
25	5C2	77,031		1
26	5C7a	24,830	If the answer is incorrect, award **1 mark** for the formal method of long multiplication which contains no more than **ONE** arithmetic error.	2
27	6C7b	34	Award **2 marks** for the correct answer of 34. If the answer is incorrect, award **1 mark** for a formal method of division with no more than **ONE** arithmetic error, e.g. • long division algorithm, e.g. 16) 544 = 34 r 10 − 480 (30 × 16) 74 (error) − 64 (4 × 16) 10 **OR** 16) 544 = 33 (error) − 480 (30 × 16) 64 − 64 (4 × 16) 0 • short division algorithm, e.g. 16) 54⁵4 = 33 r 6 (error in carrying digit)	2
28	5C2	104,179		1
29	6C7b	568	If the answer is incorrect, award **1 mark** for the formal method of division which contains no more than **ONE** arithmetic error.	2
30	6F5b	$\frac{3}{10}$		1
31	6C9	120		1
32	6F5a	$\frac{3}{10}$	Accept equivalent fraction **OR exact** decimal 0.3	1
33	6F4	$\frac{19}{20}$		1
34	5C6a	120		1
35	6R2	810		1
36	6F5b	15		1

Test 1 Paper 2: Reasoning

<table>
<tr><th>Qu.</th><th>Content domain</th><th>Requirement</th><th>Additional guidance</th><th>Mark</th></tr>
<tr><td>1</td><td>5C5c</td><td>19; 2; and 11 circled</td><td></td><td>1</td></tr>
<tr><td>2</td><td>6G2a</td><td><table><tr><td></td><td>Fewer than 6 vertices</td><td>6 or more vertices</td></tr><tr><td>1 or more square faces</td><td>C</td><td>A</td></tr><tr><td>No square faces</td><td>D</td><td>B
E</td></tr></table></td><td></td><td>1</td></tr>
<tr><td>3</td><td>4N4b</td><td>96,840
96,800
97,000</td><td>Award 2 marks for all three numbers rounded. Award 1 mark for two numbers correctly rounded.</td><td>2</td></tr>
<tr><td>4</td><td>5M5</td><td>2,500 ml
3 litres
5 litres
5,250 ml</td><td></td><td>1</td></tr>
<tr><td>5</td><td>4M7a</td><td>27</td><td>Award 2 marks for the correct answer of 27 cm.
If the answer is incorrect, award 1 mark for evidence of appropriate working, e.g.
70 cm – (8 cm × 2) = 70 cm – 16 m = 54 ÷ 2 =</td><td>2</td></tr>
<tr><td>6</td><td>6F11</td><td><table><tr><td>Fraction</td><td>$\frac{3}{4}$</td><td>$\frac{3}{5}$</td><td>$\frac{1}{10}$</td><td>$\frac{99}{100}$</td></tr><tr><td>Decimal</td><td>0.75</td><td>0.6</td><td>0.1</td><td>0.99</td></tr><tr><td>Percentage</td><td>75%</td><td>60%</td><td>10%</td><td>99%</td></tr></table></td><td>Award 2 marks for all correct.
Award 1 mark for at least five correct OR award 1 mark for all correct except that $\frac{3}{4}$ and $\frac{1}{10}$ are not written in their simplest form but are equivalent.</td><td>2</td></tr>
<tr><td>7</td><td>5C5d</td><td><table><tr><td>20</td><td></td><td></td><td></td><td></td><td></td></tr><tr><td>25</td><td></td><td>35</td><td></td><td></td><td></td></tr><tr><td></td><td>36</td><td></td><td>48</td><td></td><td></td></tr><tr><td></td><td></td><td>49</td><td></td><td></td><td></td></tr><tr><td></td><td></td><td></td><td>64</td><td></td><td></td></tr><tr><td>45</td><td></td><td></td><td></td><td>81</td><td></td></tr><tr><td></td><td></td><td>70</td><td></td><td></td><td>100</td></tr></table></td><td></td><td>1</td></tr>
<tr><td>8</td><td>5M9d</td><td>12</td><td>Award 2 marks for the correct answer of 12 jugs of water.
If the answer is incorrect, award 1 mark for evidence of appropriate working, e.g.
3 litres × 1,000 = 3,000 ml
3,000 ÷ 250 =</td><td>2</td></tr>
<tr><td>9</td><td>4N5</td><td>–12   –8   –2   0   9   12</td><td></td><td>1</td></tr>
<tr><td>10</td><td>5S1</td><td>15:55</td><td></td><td>1</td></tr>
</table>

11	5C4/5C8c	900	Award **2 marks** for the correct answer of 900 leaflets. If the answer is incorrect, award **1 mark** for evidence of appropriate working, e.g. 3,600 leaflets – (900 × 2) leaflets = 1,800 leaflets ÷ 2 = wrong answer	2
12	6G4a	35		1
13	6R1	£4.17	Award **2 marks** for correct answer £4.17. Award **1 mark** for evidence of a method. Correct answer need not be obtained for the award of **1 mark**.	2
14	5M4	170 minutes		1
15	5C4/5C6a	6	Award **2 marks** for the correct answer of 6. If the answer is incorrect, award **1 mark** for evidence of an appropriate method, e.g. 5 × 7 = 35 35 – 5 = 30 30 ÷ 5 =	2
16	5F2a	mixed number $3\frac{1}{2}$, improper fraction $\frac{7}{2}$		1
17	3G3b	cube		1
18	5N3b	64		1
19	4F8 4F6b	**a)** 2.22 = 2 ones, 2 tenths and 2 hundredths, which is less than 2.42 = 2 ones, 4 tenths and 2 hundredths **b)** $\frac{3}{10}$ — 0.3 $\frac{3}{100}$ — 0.03 $\frac{3}{10}$ — 3.0		1 1
20	5S2	a) 1 May and 1 June b) 0.225		1 1
21	6A3	b = 10a – 3		1
22	6F9b	200		1
23	6A2	56.25		1
24	5S1	NO and an explanation that shows: • she can take the 12:37 train and change at Great Hills, **OR** • she can take the 13:12, which arrives at Lower Vales 21 minutes before 2:45 p.m, **OR** • 2:45 p.m. is 14:45, so the 13:12 will get her there in time.	Award **1 mark** for correct answer NO. **Do not award** any marks for simply circling NO or rewording the question to say that it is not the latest train without explaining why.	1
25	6R2	18	Award **2 marks** for correct answer 18. Award **1 mark** for evidence of an appropriate method, e.g. 50% of 60 = 30 30 ÷ 5 × 3 = wrong answer Correct answer need not be obtained for the award of **1 mark**.	2

Test 1 Paper 3: Reasoning

Qu.	Content domain	Requirement	Additional guidance	Mark
1	5N1	170; 210		1
2	5C5a	53 and 28 circled		1
3	5C6b	=, <, >		1
4	3C4/3C8	90	Award **2 marks** for the correct answer of 90. If the answer is incorrect, award **1 mark** for evidence of an appropriate method, e.g. $6 \times 5 = 30$ $120 - 30 =$	2
5	5F7	8 9 8 9	Award **2 marks** for all values correct as shown. If the answer is incorrect, award **1 mark** for three numbers correctly rounded.	2
6	4N2a	E C A B D	Award **2 marks** for all four prices correctly placed. Award **1 mark** for two prices correctly placed.	2
7	4M7b			1
8	6A3	2,150; The rule is 'add 400'.		1
9	6F6/5C6b	2nd and 3rd statements ticked		1
10	3C6	× : 7, 12 4 : 28, 48 8 : 56, 96	Award **2 marks** for all three correct missing numbers. Award **1 mark** for two correct missing numbers.	2
11	6F4	1 $2\frac{5}{7}$	Award **1 mark** for each correct fraction.	2
12	5M9a	10p	Award **2 marks** for correct answer 10p. If the answer is incorrect, award **1 mark** for evidence of an appropriate method, e.g. £4.80 ÷ 6 = 80p £3.60 ÷ 4 = error Error – 80p = error Correct answer need not be obtained for the award of **1 mark**.	2
13	6G4b	$a = 133$ $b = 68$		2
14	6S3	a) 12 b) 18		1 1
15	4C2	3 0 8 7 + 1 4 3 3 4 5 2 0		1

<table>
<tr><td>16</td><td>5M9</td><td>£4.75</td><td>Award 2 marks for the correct answer of £4.75.
If the answer is incorrect, award 1 mark for evidence of appropriate working, e.g.
£20 – £6.50 – £8.75 = wrong answer
OR
£6.50 + £8.75 = £15.25
£20 – £15.25 = wrong answer
Accept 1 mark for £475 OR £475p as evidence of appropriate working.
Working must be carried through to reach an answer for the award of 1 mark.</td><td>2</td></tr>
<tr><td>17</td><td>5S1

6F9</td><td>a) All correct equivalents required<table><tr><td></td><td>Jun</td><td>Kyle</td><td>Anna</td><td>Jem</td></tr><tr><td>Length (m)</td><td>1.8</td><td>1.5</td><td>1.2</td><td>0.5</td></tr></table>b) 0.3</td><td></td><td>1

1</td></tr>
<tr><td>18</td><td>5M4</td><td>Award 1 mark for an explanation that shows that an extra lot of 20 minutes is needed by Kayla, e.g. Jon parked for 1 hour 40 minutes and there are 5 lots of 20 minutes in 1 hour 40 minutes. As 1 hour 45 minutes is 5 minutes longer, Kayla will need to pay another 45p for another lot of 20 minutes.</td><td>Do not award any marks for simply re-stating that Kayla paid 45p more than Jon.</td><td>1</td></tr>
<tr><td>19</td><td>6R2</td><td>80</td><td>Award 2 marks for the correct answer of 80.
If the answer is incorrect, award 1 mark for evidence of appropriate working, e.g.
100 × 4 = 400
20 + 20 + 20 + 20 = wrong answer
OR
100 × 4 = 400
400 ÷ 5 = wrong answer</td><td>2</td></tr>
<tr><td>20</td><td>5M9b</td><td>100</td><td></td><td>1</td></tr>
<tr><td>21</td><td>5C7a</td><td>287</td><td>Award 3 marks for correct answer 287 cm^3.
Award 2 marks for a correct method but with one arithmetic error, e.g.
cuboid 7 × 15 × 6cm = error
cube 7 × 7 × 7 cm = 343 cm^3
error – 343 = error carried through.
Award 1 mark for sight of 343 (volume of cube in cm^3) and 630 (volume of cuboid in cm^3).
Do not award any marks if the error is in the place value of the multiplication.</td><td>3</td></tr>
</table>

Test 2 Paper 1: Arithmetic

Qu.	Content domain	Requirement	Additional guidance	Mark
1	3C2	1,332		1
2	3N2b	2,664		1
3	3C1	165		1
4	3F4	$\frac{8}{9}$		1
5	3C1	6,300		1
6	5C1	995		1
7	4C6a	12		1
8	4C2	5,600		1
9	6C7a	27,230	Award **2 marks** for the correct answer of 27,230. If the answer is incorrect, award **1 mark** for a formal method of long multiplication with no more than **ONE** arithmetic error, e.g. 1945 × 14 7780 19450 27235 (error) **OR** 1945 × 14 7780 19480 (error) 27260 Working must be carried through to reach a final answer for the award of **1 mark**. **Do not** award any marks if the error is in the place value, e.g. the omission of the zero when multiplying the tens. 1945 × 14 7780 1948 (error) 9728	2
10	4F4	$1\frac{4}{5}$	Accept equivalent fraction **OR exact** decimal 1.8	1
11	5C6a	40		1
12	4C2	2,920		1
13	6F9b	2.7		1
14	4C6b	120		1
15	4F10a	36		1
16	5F10	4.68		1
17	6R2	600		1
18	5C7b	859		1

19	6C7b	24	Award **2 marks** for the correct answer of 24. If the answer is incorrect, award **1 mark** for a formal method of division with no more than **ONE** arithmetic error, i.e. long division algorithm, e.g. 2 4 r 1 0 1 7 ⟌ 4 0 8 – 3 4 0 (20 × 17) 7 8 (error) – 6 8 (4 × 17) 1 0 **OR** 2 3 (error) 1 7 ⟌ 4 0 8 – 3 4 0 (20 × 17) 6 8 – 6 8 (4 × 17) 0 • short division algorithm, e.g. 2 3 r 7 17 ⟌ 4 0 ^{5}8 (error in carrying digit)	2
20	6F4	$\frac{9}{6}$ **OR** $\frac{3}{2}$ **OR** $1\frac{1}{2}$		1
21	6C9	56		1
22	5C6b	1.92		1
23	5C7a	34,356		1
24	5F10	11.27		1
25	6F10	270		1
26	6F9b	58.8		1
27	5C6a	120		1
28	6F4	$9\frac{7}{12}$		1
29	5C7a	5,074	If the answer is incorrect, award **1 mark** for the formal method of long multiplication which contains no more than **one** arithmetic error.	2
30	6C7b	84	If the answer is incorrect, award **1 mark** for the formal method of division which contains no more than **one** arithmetic error.	2
31	5C5d	150		1
32	5C2	354,864		1
33	6F5a	$\frac{1}{8}$	Accept equivalent fraction **OR exact** decimal 0.125	1
34	6C9	4		1
35	6R2	306		1
36	6F5b	$\frac{3}{20}$	Accept equivalent fraction **OR exact** decimal 0.15	1

Test 2 Paper 2: Reasoning

Qu.	Content domain	Requirement	Additional guidance	Mark
1	4C6a	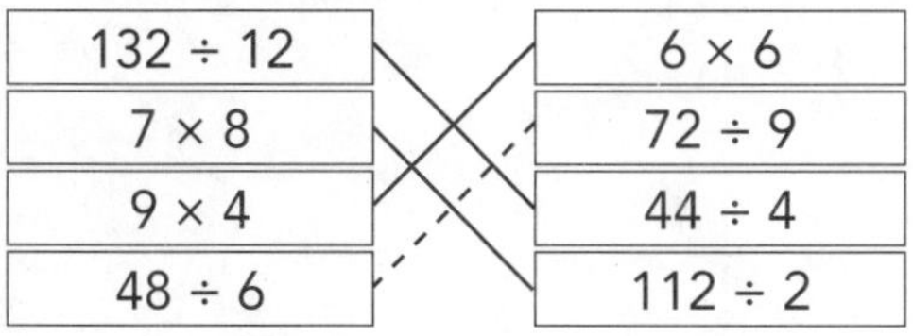 132 ÷ 12 6 × 6 7 × 8 72 ÷ 9 9 × 4 44 ÷ 4 48 ÷ 6 112 ÷ 2	All correctly matched for the mark.	1
2	4G2b	A, C, D and E		1
3	5C8b	194	Award **2 marks** for the correct answer of 194. If the answer is incorrect, award **1 mark** for evidence of an appropriate method, e.g. 7 × 8 = 28 (error) 250 – 28 =	2
4	6F11	$\frac{14}{20}$ circled		1
5	5F10	1.4		1
6	5C8a	7		1
7	3M9 3M9d	a) Water level clearly drawn halfway between 600 ml and 800 ml. b) 1.3		1 1
8	4F10b	£6	Award **2 marks** for the correct answer of £6. If the answer is incorrect, award **1 mark** for evidence of an appropriate method, e.g. £1.60 + £0.40 = £2 £2 × 3 =	2
9	4M4c 4M5	a) 230 b) 480		1 1
10	6R4	250	Award **2 marks** for correct answer 250 g. If the answer is incorrect, award **1 mark** for evidence of an appropriate method, e.g. 750 ÷ 150 = 5 50 g × 5 = error Correct answer need not be obtained for the award of **1 mark**.	2
11	4S2	a) £125 b) February and April		1 1
12	5C5a 5C5d	a) Any multiple of 12 b) Any multiple of 12, excluding the answer given in a) and also 36, since this is the answer for c). c) 36	Award **2 marks** for all correct. Award **1 mark** for any two correct (answer is incorrect if also used as an answer for another question).	2
13	6N5	–16 –4	Award **1 mark** for each correct missing number.	2
14	5F4	A, C, E ticked		1
15	6N2 6N3	a) 4,999,995 b) 4,900,000		1 1

16	5M7a	131		1
17	5G3b	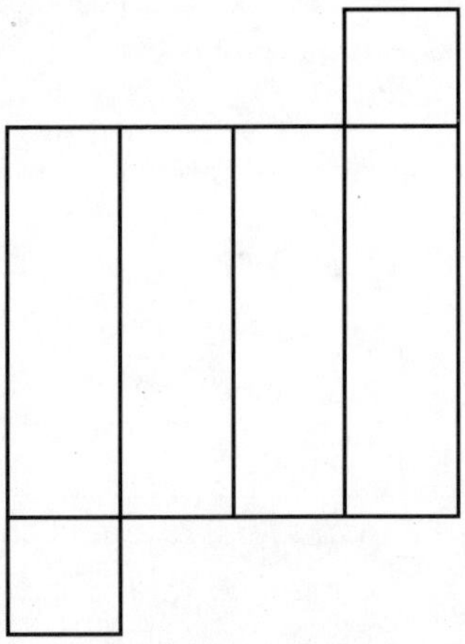		1
18	6S1	301	Award **2 marks** for the correct answer of 301. If the answer is incorrect, award **1 mark** for evidence of an appropriate method, e.g. 267 + 437 + 312 + 265 + 259 + 266 1806 ÷ 6 =	2
19	5P2	The triangle has moved **6** squares to the left and **5** squares up.		1
20	5M7b	40	Award **2 marks** for the correct answer of 40 cm^2. If the answer is incorrect, award **1 mark** for evidence of an appropriate method, e.g. $(2 \times 2) + (12 \times 3)$ **OR** $(12 \times 5) - (2 \times 10)$	2
21	6F3	$\frac{18}{15}$ $1\frac{2}{3}$ $1\frac{4}{5}$		1
22	6A4	$m = 20$ and $n = 5$	Award **3 marks** for correct answer $m = 20$ and $n = 5$. Award **2 marks** for correctly identifying n as 5 and a correct method to calculate m with only one arithmetic error, e.g. $3m \div 10 = 6$ $3m = 60$ $60 \div 3 =$ error Award **1 mark** for correctly identifying n as 5.	3

Test 2 Paper 3: Reasoning

<table>
<tr><th>Qu.</th><th>Content domain</th><th>Requirement</th><th>Additional guidance</th><th>Mark</th></tr>
<tr><td>1</td><td>6N3</td><td> 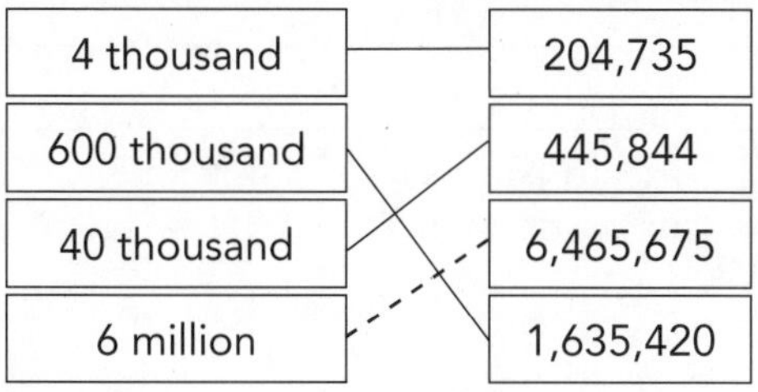4 thousand — 204,735
600 thousand — 1,635,420
40 thousand — 445,844
6 million — 6,465,675</td><td>Award 1 mark for all correctly matched.</td><td>1</td></tr>
<tr><td>2</td><td>3G2</td><td>C</td><td></td><td>1</td></tr>
<tr><td>3</td><td>4C2</td><td>1,985</td><td>Award 2 marks for the correct answer of 1,985.
If the answer is incorrect, award 1 mark for evidence of an appropriate method, e.g.
9,999 – 4,028 – 3,986 = 1,985
OR
9,999 – (4,028 + 3,986) = 1,985</td><td>2</td></tr>
<tr><td>4</td><td>5N2</td><td>45,501 and 50,000 circled</td><td></td><td>1</td></tr>
<tr><td>5</td><td>6N5</td><td>–3°C circled</td><td></td><td>1</td></tr>
<tr><td>6</td><td>4C2</td><td>308</td><td>Award 2 marks for the correct answer of 308.
If the answer is incorrect, award 1 mark for evidence of an appropriate method, e.g. (978 + 1,235) green apples – (1,305 + 600) red apples = 2,213 green apples – 1,905 red apples, but for an incorrect answer.</td><td>2</td></tr>
<tr><td>7</td><td>5C6b</td><td>8.5 ÷ 100 = 0.085
8.5 × 10 = 85
8.5 × 1000 = 8,500</td><td>Award 2 marks for all three calculations completed correctly, as shown.
Award 1 mark for two correct calculations.</td><td>2</td></tr>
<tr><td>8</td><td>5F4</td><td>a) $\frac{7}{10} + \frac{1}{2}$
b) $\frac{7}{5} - \frac{3}{10}$</td><td></td><td>1
1</td></tr>
<tr><td>9</td><td>4F10a</td><td>48 books</td><td></td><td>1</td></tr>
<tr><td>10</td><td>4G2b</td><td> 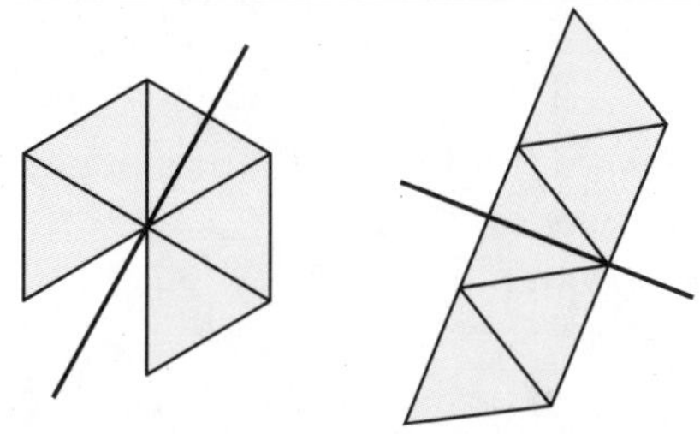</td><td></td><td>1</td></tr>
<tr><td>11</td><td>5M5</td><td><table><tr><th>Fruits and vegetables</th><th>Grams</th><th>Kilograms</th></tr><tr><td>potatoes</td><td>5,500</td><td>5.5</td></tr><tr><td>apples</td><td>2,500</td><td>2.5</td></tr><tr><td>grapes</td><td>350</td><td>0.35</td></tr><tr><td>ginger</td><td>60</td><td>0.06</td></tr></table></td><td>Award 2 marks for the table completed as shown.
Award 1 mark for two of the three numbers completed correctly.</td><td>2</td></tr>
<tr><td>12</td><td>6G4a</td><td>$x = 35$</td><td></td><td>1</td></tr>
</table>

13	6C9	a) 2 b) 298		1 1
14	6A2	a) 8 b) 18		1 2
15	3C4	680 and 295		1
16	6S1	YES	Award **2 marks** for correct answer YES and an explanation that: • lime and lemon juice are $\frac{2}{8}$ of the total juice sold and orange is $\frac{1}{4}$ and that $\frac{2}{8}$ is the same as $\frac{1}{4}$, **OR** • lime and lemon both sold $\frac{1}{8}$ of the total juices and $\frac{2}{8}$ is equal to $\frac{1}{4}$, **OR** • $\frac{1}{4}$ is equal to $\frac{2}{8}$, **OR** • the lemon and lime slices of the pie chart put together are the same size as the slice for the orange. Award **1 mark** for YES and recognition that lime and lemon equal $\frac{2}{8}$, but no reference to the orange juice. **Do not award** any marks for saying that the lemon and lime are both the same size or equal.	2
17	5C8a	16 and 144		1
18	6F10	a) 3 b) 3.5 c) 3.49		1
19	4P3a 6P2	a) (5,9) b) **B** (−4,1) **C** (2,1)		1 1
20	6R3	50		1
21	5M6	a) 9 b) 1.1		1 1
22	6G5 6M9	12.5	Award **2 marks** for correct answer 12.5 cm. Award **1 mark** for a correct method **or** for an answer of 125, e.g. 750 mm ÷ 3 = error error ÷ 2 = error Correct answer need not be obtained for the award of **1 mark**.	2
23	6R1	0.8	Award **2 marks** for correct answer 0.8. Award **1 mark** for correct method, e.g. 1.2 × 2 = 2.4 (value of two squares) 2.4 ÷ 3 = error Correct answer need not be obtained for the award of **1 mark**.	2

Answers and spelling transcripts

Test 1, Paper 1: questions

<table>
<tr><th>Qu.</th><th>Content domain</th><th>Answer</th><th>Marking guidance</th><th>Mark</th></tr>
<tr><td>1</td><td>G5.1 – capital letters</td><td>circle: april; scotland</td><td>1 mark for two correct answers</td><td>1</td></tr>
<tr><td>2</td><td>G2.1 – statements; G2.3 – commands</td><td><table>
<tr><th>Sentence</th><th>Statement</th><th>Command</th></tr>
<tr><td>Today, the train will leave earlier than usual.</td><td>✔</td><td></td></tr>
<tr><td>Tomorrow, go to your grandma's after school.</td><td></td><td>✔</td></tr>
<tr><td>Yesterday, we climbed a tree.</td><td>✔</td><td></td></tr>
<tr><td>Bring your sports kit for the match this afternoon.</td><td></td><td>✔</td></tr>
</table></td><td>1 mark for four correct answers</td><td>1</td></tr>
<tr><td>3</td><td>G1.5b – relative pronouns</td><td>circle: who</td><td></td><td>1</td></tr>
<tr><td>4</td><td>G1.7 – prepositions</td><td>from</td><td></td><td>1</td></tr>
<tr><td>5</td><td>G1.3 – adjectives</td><td>tick: adjective</td><td></td><td>1</td></tr>
<tr><td>6</td><td>G3.2 – noun phrases</td><td>underline: the new climbing frame in the playground</td><td>All of the noun phrase must be underlined – no more, no less.</td><td>1</td></tr>
<tr><td>7</td><td>G4.1b – verbs in perfect form</td><td>circle: have been</td><td></td><td>1</td></tr>
<tr><td>8</td><td>G2.3 – commands</td><td>Open the window as it is very hot. OR Open the window.</td><td>Correct use of capital letter and full stop is required for the mark.</td><td>1</td></tr>
<tr><td>9</td><td>G1.1 – nouns</td><td>circle: Jess; ideas; food; school</td><td>1 mark for four correct answers</td><td>1</td></tr>
<tr><td>10</td><td>G5.1 – capital letters</td><td>On Monday we will visit Buckingham Palace.</td><td>1 mark for four correct answers</td><td>1</td></tr>
<tr><td>11</td><td>G4.1b – verbs in perfect form</td><td>circle: has worked; tried; have made</td><td>1 mark for three correct answers</td><td>1</td></tr>
<tr><td>12</td><td>G1.9 – subject and object</td><td>underline: the ball; the wheelbarrow; it</td><td>1 mark for three correct answers
Also accept answers that do not include 'the'.</td><td>1</td></tr>
<tr><td>13</td><td>G1.4 – conjunctions</td><td>Accept the correct insertion of an appropriate subordinating conjunction, e.g. while; whilst; as; when.</td><td>Do not accept misspellings of the subordinating conjunction.</td><td>1</td></tr>
<tr><td>14</td><td>G1.5 – pronouns</td><td>circle: his; him</td><td>1 mark for two correct answers</td><td>1</td></tr>
</table>

<table>
<tr><td>15</td><td>G5.6b – commas after fronted adverbials</td><td>Full of wonder, we all gazed at the shooting star.</td><td></td><td>1</td></tr>
<tr><td>16</td><td>G6.1 – synonyms and antonyms</td><td>swift rapid
fasten secure
immerse soak
issue concern</td><td>1 mark for four correct answers</td><td>1</td></tr>
<tr><td>17</td><td>G4.4 – passive and active</td><td><table><tr><th>Sentence</th><th>Active</th><th>Passive</th></tr><tr><td>The seals were fed from a bucket of fish.</td><td></td><td>✓</td></tr><tr><td>Kangaroos use their tails to balance.</td><td>✓</td><td></td></tr><tr><td>Some trees are planted by squirrels burying nuts.</td><td></td><td>✓</td></tr></table></td><td>1 mark for three correct answers</td><td>1</td></tr>
<tr><td>18</td><td>G6.2 – prefixes</td><td>im possible
ir responsible
in attentive
il legal</td><td>1 mark for four correct answers</td><td>1</td></tr>
<tr><td>19</td><td>G5.7 – inverted commas</td><td>tick: Anna said that butterflies can see only three colours.</td><td></td><td>1</td></tr>
<tr><td>20</td><td>G7.1 – Standard English</td><td>Can I have one of those/these/the cakes?</td><td>Capital letter and question mark use must be correct for 1 mark.</td><td>1</td></tr>
<tr><td>21</td><td>G1.6 – adverbs</td><td>circle: definitely</td><td></td><td>1</td></tr>
<tr><td>22</td><td>G1.6a – adverbials</td><td>Accept a suitable phrase that makes sense, e.g. Every night; Early in the morning; Without being asked.</td><td>Do not accept a subordinate clause, e.g. When I get up.</td><td>1</td></tr>
<tr><td>23</td><td>G3.1a – relative clauses</td><td>tick: that guarded the magical mountain.</td><td></td><td>1</td></tr>
<tr><td>24</td><td>G3.1 – sentences and clauses</td><td>tick: as a main clause</td><td></td><td>1</td></tr>
<tr><td>25</td><td>G5.8 – apostrophes</td><td>should've</td><td></td><td>1</td></tr>
<tr><td>26</td><td>G5.7 – inverted commas</td><td>The scientist said, "I am pleased with my discovery."
OR "I am pleased with my discovery," said the scientist.
OR "I am pleased with my discovery." (without the scientist said).</td><td>Inverted commas, commas and full stops must be correctly placed. Capital letters must be used correctly.</td><td>1</td></tr>
<tr><td>27</td><td>G4.1d – present and past progressive</td><td>tick: were twinkling</td><td></td><td>1</td></tr>
<tr><td>28</td><td>G5.11 – semi-colons</td><td>There was a parade in the road outside school; we all went out to have a look.</td><td></td><td>1</td></tr>
<tr><td>29</td><td>G4.1b – verbs in perfect form</td><td>had planted</td><td></td><td>1</td></tr>
</table>

30	**G5.6a – commas to clarify meaning**	**Accept** answers that explain that in the second sentence Kate will be chased, or that she is not being spoken to directly. For example, without the comma it means that they will chase Kate.		1
31	**G4.3 – subjunctive verb forms**	listen		1
32	**G5.9 – punctuation for parenthesis**	tick: Venus – the brightest planet in our sky – can sometimes be seen without a telescope.		1
33	**G2.4 – exclamations**	tick: What an amazing friend you are		1
34	**G5.8 apostrophes**	circle: Fred's		1
35	**G6.1 – synonyms and antonyms**	circle: present, absent		1
36	**G7.1 – Standard English**	tick: I swam with the school team in the competition.		1
37	**G1.8 – determiners**	determiner(s)		1
38	**G1.5 – pronouns**	he we/they	**1 mark** for **two** correct answers	1
39	**G1.9 – subject and object**	tick: Luke		1
40	**G1.5b – relative pronouns**	circle: who		1
41	**G2.2 – questions**	Are they waiting for the train?	**Accept** answers that include a correctly formed question mark and include a capital letter. **Do not accept** answers with omitted words or additional words.	1
42	**G5.10 – colons**	tick: I bought some new stationery: pencils, a ruler, a selection of pens and a pencil case.		1
43	**G5.7 – inverted commas**	tick box before 'Freddie' and after 'there,'	**1 mark** for **two** correct answers	1
44	**G3.4 – subordinating conjunctions and subordinate clauses**	tick: <u>Because you are late</u>, we have changed the song!		1
45	**G5.11 – semi-colons**	tick: semi-colon		1
46	**G1.6 – adverbs**	circle: soon		1
47	**G5.6b – commas after fronted adverbials**	Last Wednesday, we won the singing competition at the town hall.	Comma must be correctly formed.	1

48	**G5.9 – punctuation for parenthesis**	The largest river in the world is the Amazon River (6,992 km) in South America.		1
49	**G6.3 – suffixes**	enjoyable enjoyment	Must be correctly spelled and use a lower case letter.	1
50	**G1.4 – conjunctions**	circle: but, or	**1 mark** for **two** correct answers	1

Test 1, Paper 2: spelling task transcript

Spelling one: The word is **transplanting**.
We are **transplanting** the bulbs from their pots to the garden.

Spelling two: The word is **positive**.
There was a **positive** response to your idea.

Spelling three: The word is **considerable**.
The new road has made a **considerable** difference to the traffic problem.

Spelling four: The word is **dough**.
To bake bread, you first need to make a **dough**.

Spelling five: The word is **official**.
We have designed an **official** programme for the concert.

Spelling six: The word is **length**.
Our snake is growing in **length** each month.

Spelling seven: The word is **government**.
The **government** has introduced a new law.

Spelling eight: The word is **adventure**.
My favourite book is full of **adventure** stories.

Spelling nine: The word is **advise**.
Your dentist will **advise** you on how to care for your teeth.

Spelling ten: The word is **obedient**.
It is helpful if your dog is trained to be **obedient**.

Spelling eleven: The word is **awkward**.
There was an **awkward** pause after Tom's joke.

Spelling twelve: The word is **coiled**.
The rope should be **coiled** up tidily after you use it.

Spelling thirteen: The word is **necessary**.
It is **necessary** to wear a safety helmet in the caves.

Spelling fourteen: The word is **travelled**.
They **travelled** through the night to arrive on time.

Spelling fifteen: The word is **piece**.
That is a lovely **piece** of fabric.

Spelling sixteen: The word is **peculiar**.
There was a **peculiar** smell in the garden shed.

Spelling seventeen: The word is **cough**.
I went to the doctor because I had a **cough**.

Spelling eighteen: The word is **island**.
When I was on holiday, we sailed to an **island**.

Spelling nineteen: The word is **nutritious**.
It is very important that you eat a **nutritious** lunch.

Spelling twenty: The word is **inconceivable**.
My Dad found the idea quite **inconceivable**.

Test 2, Paper 1: questions

Qu.	Content domain	Answer	Marking guidance	Mark
1	**G5.8 – apostrophes**	he'd	**Do not accept** answers that omit or misplace the apostrophe.	1
2	**G5.1 – capital letters**	circle: friday; molly's	**1 mark** for **two** correct answers	1
3	**G1.6 – adverbs**	**Accept** an answer that is a plausible, correctly spelled adverb, e.g. *quickly*; *slowly*; *nervously*; *confidently*.		1
4	**G5.8 – apostrophes**	tick: Can I borrow Jamila's bicycle? At the start of the race, all of the cars' engines were revving noisily.	**1 mark** for **two** correct answers	1
5	**G5.6a – commas to clarify meaning**	tick box after: dancing		1

6	**G3.3 – coordinating conjunctions**	or; and; but	**1 mark** for **three** correct answers	1
7	**G1.2 – verbs**	underline: do; patrol; protect	**1 mark** for **three** correct answers	1
8	**G1.8 – determiners**	an; an; a	**1 mark** for **three** correct answers	1
9	**G4.1b – verbs in perfect form**	circle: had started		1
10	**G1.5b – relative pronouns**	tick: where		1
11	**G4.1d – present and past progressive**	were listening; were building	**1 mark** for **two** correct answers	1
12	**G7.2 - Formal and informal vocabulary, G7.3 - Formal and informal structures**	tick: Daily exercise should be promoted for all.		1
13	**G5.7 – inverted commas**	tick boxes after: announced; town	**1 mark** for **two** correct answers	1
14	**G1.1 – nouns, G1.2 – verbs, G1.3 – adjectives, G1.7 – prepositions**	destruction (N) in (P) awful (A) said (V)	**1 mark** for **four** correct answers	1
15	**G5.8 – apostrophes**	**Accept** answers that refer to possession, e.g. the idea is from Oscar.		1
16	**G6.3 – suffixes**	appoint ment bitter ness hair less dread ful	**1 mark** for **four** correct answers	1
17	**G2.2 - Questions, G5.3 - Question marks**	**Accept** a grammatically correct and accurately punctuated question, e.g. Is the team in the final round? OR Are the team in the final? OR Do you know if the team are in the final round?	**Also accept** a correctly constructed and punctuated question that is enclosed in inverted commas. **Do not accept** the addition of a reporting clause resulting in a question contained within a statement, Elsie asked, "Is the team in the final round?"	1
18	**G2.3 – commands**	underline: run; leave	**1 mark** for **two** correct answers	1
19	**G5.5 – commas in lists**	tick: to separate items in a list		1
20	**G6.1 – synonyms and antonyms**	tick: separate		1
21	**G1.9 - Subject and object**	**Accept:** The football manager posed for a photograph. The football manager posed for a photograph. The football manager posed for a photograph.		1

22	**G5.10 – colons**	tick: We saw beautiful landscapes on our trip: mountains, lakes and coasts.		**1**
23	**G2.3 – commands**	tick: Bring a packed lunch so you do not get hungry.		**1**
24	**G3.4 – subordinating conjunctions and subordinate clauses**	circle: even though it might be a little scary at first		**1**
25	**G3.4 – subordinating conjunctions and subordinate clauses G1.7 – prepositions, G1.4 – conjunctions**	tick: I'd like to finish my book before we go out. The phone stopped ringing before I could answer it.	**1 mark** for **two** correct answers	**1**
26	**G1.5 – pronouns**	circle: his; He; them	**1 mark** for **three** correct answers	**1**
27	**G6.1 – synonyms and antonyms**	influence persuade courteous polite confine imprison accusation blame thanks gratitude	**1 mark** for **five** correct answers	**1**
28	**G1.3 - Adjectives, G1.6 - Adverbs**	careful - Adjective carefully - Adverb	No spelling requirements	**1**
29	**G4.1b – verbs in perfect form**	had		**1**
30	**G4.3 – subjunctive verb forms**	tick: I would drive more slowly if I were you.		**1**
31	**G1.6a – adverbials**	underline: During the match	**Accept** other means of indicating the answer, e.g. circling.	**1**
32	**G5.14 – bullet points**	**Accept** in any order: • scissors • coloured paper • glue	**Also accept** capitalisation of the three items and/or consistent use of commas or semi-colons after the first two items if accompanied by a full stop after the third. **Do not accept** inconsistent use of punctuation or capitalisation.	**1**
33	**G1.5 – pronouns**	tick: pronouns		**1**
34	**G4.1a – simple past and simple present**	walked; sang; brought	**1 mark** for **three** correct answers. Answer must be lower case and correctly spelled.	**1**

35	**G5.1 – capital letters**	tick: The teacher took the children to the library in the middle of Newcastle.		**1**
36	**G2.2 – questions**	tick: Can you tell me what time it opens at		**1**
37	**G1.5a – possessive pronouns**	circle: her		**1**
38	**G3.2 - Noun phrases**	**Accept:** Noun phrase Expanded noun phrase Complement	No spelling requirements	**1**
39	**G1.2 – verbs**	tick: Can you light the candles please?		**1**
40	**G2.1 – statements; G2.2 – questions; G2.3 – commands; G2.4 – exclamations**	You have been to that art gallery, haven't you question The art gallery is open now statement How amazing the art is in this gallery exclamation Go into the gift shop in the gallery command	**1 mark** for **four** correct answers	**1**
41	**G6.2 – prefixes**	im	Must be correctly spelled.	**1**
42	**G1.7 – prepositions**	tick: He walked across the road. We struggled to climb over the fence.	**1 mark** for **two** correct answers	**1**
43a	**G5.9 – punctuation for parenthesis**	commas		**1**
43b	**G5.9 – punctuation for parenthesis**	brackets or dashes	Accept either answer.	**1**
44	**G5.11 – semi-colons**	There will be a huge celebration party next week; it will probably be on Monday.		**1**
45	**G3.2 – noun phrases**	**Accept** answers that are a noun phrase which include three words, for example: My friend Claire Your little brother	Capital letters must be used where appropriate.	**1**
46	**G1.5a - Possessive pronouns**	circle: his		**1**
47	**G4.4 – passive and active**	The children planted the seeds.	The answer must be correctly punctuated. **Do not accept** answers with omitted words or additional words.	**1**
48	**G6.1 – synonyms and antonyms**	circle: overpriced, extortionate	**1 mark** for **two** correct answers	**1**
49	**G4.1b – verbs in perfect form**	tick: My dog was unwell, but since he has been at the vet's, he is much better.		**1**

Test 2, Paper 2: spelling task transcript

Spelling one: The word is **creased.**
That jacket is too **creased** to wear.

Spelling two: The word is **families**.
Our **families** are all getting together for a big meal.

Spelling three: The word is **environment**.
It is important to care for the **environment**.

Spelling four: The word is **appearing**.
The same bird keeps **appearing** at my window.

Spelling five: The word is **mature**.
There are **mature** trees of a hundred years old in the park.

Spelling six: The word is **collapsed**.
The bridge **collapsed** during the flood.

Spelling seven: The word is **deliberate**.
James made a **deliberate** effort to work harder.

Spelling eight: The word is **illogical**.
It would be **illogical** to make a mistake on purpose.

Spelling nine: The word is **handkerchief**.
I need a **handkerchief** because I'm going to sneeze.

Spelling ten: The word is **tongue**.
This spicy food is making my **tongue** tingle.

Spelling eleven: The word is **infectious**.
Even a cold can be **infectious**.

Spelling twelve: The word is **panel**.
You will meet the **panel** of judges before the competition.

Spelling thirteen: The word is **attendance**.
This class has a good **attendance** record.

Spelling fourteen: The word is **invisible**.
Sam's writing is so small it is almost **invisible**.

Spelling fifteen: The word is **received**.
The twins **received** lots of gifts for their birthday.

Spelling sixteen: The word is **further**.
The guide told us not to walk any **further**.

Spelling seventeen: The word is **famous**.
A **famous** author is coming to our school next month.

Spelling eighteen: The word is **architect**.
The **architect** presented her designs to the council.

Spelling nineteen: The word is **signature**.
Leave space for your **signature** at the end of the letter.

Spelling twenty: The word is **descendant**.
We looked at the family tree to identify who Prince Charles was a **descendant** of.

Test 3, Paper 1: questions

Qu.	Content domain	Answer	Marking guidance	Mark
1	**G5.1 – capital letters**	tick: The pyrenees is a range of mountains in Spain. One of England's coasts faces the atlantic Ocean.	**1 mark** for **two** correct answers	**1**
2	**G1.2 – verbs**	circle: stood; passed	**1 mark** for **two** correct answers	**1**
3	**G2.2 – question**	has she		**1**
4	**G1.1 – nouns, G1.6 – adverbs, G1.7 – prepositions G1.8 – determiners**	now (A) otters (N) in (P) the (D)	**1 mark** for **four** correct answers	**1**
5	**G3.4 – subordinating conjunctions and subordinate clauses**	circle: until; As; while	**1 mark** for **three** correct answers	**1**
6	**G1.9 – subject and object**	cows (S) grass (O) We (S) rattle (O)	**1 mark** for **four** correct answers	**1**
7	**G5.5 - Commas in lists, G5.6a - Commas to clarify meaning**	Pam's hobbies are swimming, cycling, reading and listening to music.		**1**

<table>
<tr><td>8</td><td>G5.8 – apostrophes</td><td>tick: They hadn't visited Henry's house before.
It's time to go home now.</td><td>1 mark for two correct answers</td><td>1</td></tr>
<tr><td>9</td><td>G3.2 – noun phrases</td><td>Accept any suitable noun phrase that makes sense, containing three words. Use capital letters where appropriate. For example: A new family; My friend Baljit.</td><td></td><td>1</td></tr>
<tr><td>10</td><td>G1.8 – determiners</td><td>circle: any; the; a; some</td><td>1 mark for four correct answers</td><td>1</td></tr>
<tr><td>11</td><td>G4.1c – modal verbs</td><td>tick: I will travel by plane in the morning.</td><td></td><td>1</td></tr>
<tr><td>12</td><td>G3.4 – subordinating conjunctions and subordinate clauses</td><td>tick: although</td><td></td><td>1</td></tr>
<tr><td>13</td><td>G4.4 – passive and active</td><td><table><tr><th>Sentence</th><th>Active</th><th>Passive</th></tr><tr><td>All of the paintings in the museum had been stolen.</td><td></td><td>✔</td></tr><tr><td>The thief entered through an open window.</td><td>✔</td><td></td></tr><tr><td>Some of the pictures were recovered by the police.</td><td></td><td>✔</td></tr><tr><td>Unfortunately, the robber escaped with the best ones.</td><td>✔</td><td></td></tr></table></td><td>1 mark for four correct answers</td><td>1</td></tr>
<tr><td>14</td><td>G5.7 – inverted commas</td><td>tick: "Will everyone please listen?" requested Meera.</td><td></td><td>1</td></tr>
<tr><td>15</td><td>G5.6a – commas to clarify meaning</td><td>tick: to mark the end of a clause</td><td></td><td>1</td></tr>
<tr><td>16</td><td>G4.1d – present and past progressive</td><td>tick: Ants are marching across the floor of my kitchen.
Marcus is sitting on the grass to watch the ants carrying leaves to their nest.</td><td>1 mark for two correct answers</td><td>1</td></tr>
<tr><td>17</td><td>G6.2 – prefixes</td><td>mis lead
dis integrate
over look
un necessary</td><td>1 mark for four correct answers</td><td>1</td></tr>
<tr><td>18</td><td>G5.13 – hyphens</td><td>tick: There are 300-year-old houses in my street.</td><td></td><td>1</td></tr>
<tr><td>19</td><td>G5.10 – colons</td><td>We have a number of people visiting this weekend: aunts, uncles, grandparents and cousins.</td><td></td><td>1</td></tr>
<tr><td>20</td><td>G3.3 - Co-ordinating conjunctions</td><td>Accept a grammatically correct and accurately punctuated sentence using an appropriate co-ordinating conjunction, with or without a preceding commas, e.g. and, but, yet
You can go to the cinema <u>but</u> you will need to be home by 9pm.</td><td></td><td>1</td></tr>
<tr><td>21</td><td>G1.5 – pronouns</td><td>tick: his him them</td><td></td><td>1</td></tr>
</table>

<table>
<tr><td>22</td><td>G3.1a – relative clauses</td><td>Accept answers that refer to the function of a non-defining relative clause, e.g. to add extra information, to tell us more about the cousin.</td><td></td><td>1</td></tr>
<tr><td>23</td><td>G6.3 – suffixes</td><td>ness</td><td></td><td>1</td></tr>
<tr><td>24</td><td>G5.12 – single dashes</td><td>tick: The tiger is the biggest species of the cat family – it can reach lengths of up to 3.3 metres.</td><td></td><td>1</td></tr>
<tr><td>25</td><td>G5.11 – semi-colons</td><td>
<table>
<tr><th>Sentence</th><th>Correct</th><th>Incorrect</th></tr>
<tr><td>Trekking through a jungle can be very hard work; pushing through bushes, climbing over creepers.</td><td></td><td>✔</td></tr>
<tr><td>The tops of mountains can have extreme climates; they can be extremely hot, or extremely cold.</td><td>✔</td><td></td></tr>
<tr><td>Surprisingly, a desert supports many types of plant; and wildlife.</td><td></td><td>✔</td></tr>
</table>
</td><td>1 mark for three correct answers</td><td>1</td></tr>
<tr><td>26</td><td>G4.1d – present and past progressive</td><td>were running</td><td>Accept minor slips in spelling.</td><td>1</td></tr>
<tr><td>27</td><td>G4.4 – passive and active</td><td>A lovely solo was played on the piano by Alex.
A lovely solo was played by Alex on the piano.
A lovely solo was played.</td><td>Accept answers that omit 'lovely', and those that have minor slips in spelling.</td><td>1</td></tr>
<tr><td>28</td><td>G4.1c – modal verbs</td><td>Accept answers that explain that the event is less likely to take place, e.g. might means that it is not definite.</td><td></td><td>1</td></tr>
<tr><td>29</td><td>G5.9 – punctuation for parenthesis</td><td>Golden eagles have been known to attack a variety of large animals (foxes, wild cats, deer and even goats) using their large talons and beaks.</td><td></td><td>1</td></tr>
<tr><td>30</td><td>G6.1 – synonyms and antonyms</td><td>tick: cover surround</td><td></td><td>1</td></tr>
<tr><td>31</td><td>G3.4 – subordinating conjunctions and subordinate clauses</td><td>underline: if they are caught by predators</td><td></td><td>1</td></tr>
<tr><td>32</td><td>G1.7 – prepositions, G3.4 – subordinating conjunctions and subordinate clauses</td><td>
<table>
<tr><th>Sentence</th><th>Subordinating conjunction</th><th>Preposition</th></tr>
<tr><td>Shall we go to the museum after we have seen the castle?</td><td>✔</td><td></td></tr>
<tr><td>The concert will begin after everyone has sat down.</td><td>✔</td><td></td></tr>
<tr><td>Let's make some cakes after school today.</td><td></td><td>✔</td></tr>
</table>
</td><td>1 mark for three correct answers</td><td>1</td></tr>
</table>

<table>
<tr><td>33</td><td>G1.8 – determiners</td><td>We went to a farm and I collected an apple.
We all had a fantastic time.
I hope we can go to the farm again.</td><td>1 mark for three correct answers</td><td>1</td></tr>
<tr><td>34</td><td>G1.1 – nouns</td><td>tick: nouns</td><td></td><td>1</td></tr>
<tr><td>35</td><td>G1.6a - Adverbials</td><td><u>In November</u>, our class will go away on a residential trip.</td><td></td><td>1</td></tr>
<tr><td>36</td><td>G5.8 – apostrophes</td><td>He is
I will
do not</td><td>1 mark for three correct answers.
Answers must be correctly spelled.</td><td>1</td></tr>
<tr><td>37</td><td>G5.6b – commas after fronted adverbials</td><td>tick: After half-term, swimming lessons</td><td></td><td>1</td></tr>
<tr><td>38</td><td>G3.4 – subordinating conjunctions and subordinate clauses</td><td>Accept answers with an appropriate subordinating conjunction: because</td><td>Answer must be lower case and correctly spelled.</td><td>1</td></tr>
<tr><td>39</td><td>G4.2 – tense consistency</td><td>circle: was, went</td><td></td><td>1</td></tr>
<tr><td>40</td><td>G3.1a – relative clauses</td><td>underline: who sits next to me</td><td></td><td>1</td></tr>
<tr><td>41</td><td>G1.2 – verbs</td><td>tick: Don't point, it's rude.</td><td></td><td>1</td></tr>
<tr><td>42</td><td>G2.3 – commands</td><td>Accept an answer that is a plausible command.</td><td>Answer must be correctly punctuated with either a full stop or an exclamation mark.</td><td>1</td></tr>
<tr><td>43</td><td>G2.1 – statements</td><td>tick: You can carry the equipment with a partner</td><td></td><td>1</td></tr>
<tr><td>44</td><td>G1.6 – adverbs</td><td>circle: soon</td><td></td><td>1</td></tr>
<tr><td>45</td><td>G2.4 – exclamations</td><td>tick: How amazing that present is</td><td></td><td>1</td></tr>
<tr><td>46</td><td>G7.4 – the subjunctive</td><td>tick: were</td><td></td><td>1</td></tr>
<tr><td>47</td><td>G3.2 – noun phrases</td><td>tick: as a noun phrase</td><td></td><td>1</td></tr>
<tr><td>48</td><td>G6.3 – suffixes</td><td>foxes
lorry
cacti / catuses</td><td>1 mark for three correct answers.
Answers must be lower case and correctly spelled.</td><td>1</td></tr>
<tr><td>49</td><td>G4.4 – passive and active</td><td><table>
<tr><th>Sentence</th><th>Active</th><th>Passive</th></tr>
<tr><td>The girls won the trophy.</td><td>✔</td><td></td></tr>
<tr><td>Everybody was surprised when they won.</td><td>✔</td><td></td></tr>
<tr><td>The winning goal was scored by Jess.</td><td></td><td>✔</td></tr>
</table></td><td>1 mark for three correct answers</td><td>1</td></tr>
<tr><td>50</td><td>G6.2 – prefixes</td><td>mis</td><td></td><td>1</td></tr>
</table>

Test 3, Paper 2: spelling task transcript

Spelling one: The word is **clapped**.
Everyone **clapped** at the end of the performance.

Spelling two: The word is **difficulty**.
Jo had no **difficulty** in climbing to the top of the rope.

Spelling three: The word is **imaginative**.
That's a very **imaginative** idea.

Spelling four: The word is **surrounded**.
The park is **surrounded** by bushes and trees.

Spelling five: The word is **creating**.
We are **creating** a massive collage in class.

Spelling six: The word is **weighs**.
That bag **weighs** too much for me to carry.

Spelling seven: The word is **irrelevant**.
Charlie's idea was **irrelevant** to the discussion.

Spelling eight: The word is **shoulder**.
Anna carries her bag over her **shoulder**.

Spelling nine: The word is **international**.
England has several **international** airports.

Spelling ten: The word is **probably**.
We will **probably** have a roast dinner at the weekend.

Spelling eleven: The word is **possession**.
If you have a phone in your **possession**, turn it off now.

Spelling twelve: The word is **knuckle**.
I grazed my **knuckle** when I fell over.

Spelling thirteen: The word is **conquered**.
The Romans **conquered** much of Europe.

Spelling fourteen: The word is **scenery**.
I am helping to make the **scenery** for the school play.

Spelling fifteen: The word is **neighbour**.
My **neighbour** has lost her cat.

Spelling sixteen: The word is **doubt**.
Since you have missed the train, I **doubt** you will be on time.

Spelling seventeen: The word is **transferred**.
She **transferred** everything from the boxes into the new office.

Spelling eighteen: The word is **typical**.
It was a **typical** week for Luke.

Spelling nineteen: The word is **vague**.
She had a **vague** memory of her holiday in Spain.

Spelling twenty: The word is **adventurous**.
After the residential, Sarah was known as the most **adventurous** girl.

Answers

Test 1

The story of the Minotaur

Qu.	Content domain	Answer & marking guidance	Mark
1	2a	petrifying	1
2	2d	**Award 1 mark** each for any **two** of the following: He was uncaring; cruel; selfish; wanted to look after his own people above others; scared of the Minotaur; a bully.	2
3	2b	the Minotaur	1
4	2c	Cannot allow the sacrifice to continue. / So it is the last time young citizens will be eaten. / To break the ritual of sending young citizens. / Because he wants to try to defeat the Minotaur.	1
5	2g	He was cruel.	1
6	2f	**Award 2 marks** for a developed response to the changing of the sails and the meaning of this. The paragraph is about the king asking Theseus to change the sails to white to show he was safe. The final paragraph is about Theseus forgetting to change the sails to white. **Award 1 mark** for a response to the changing of the sails.	2
7	2b	To put white sails on the ship.	1
8	2b	**Award 1 mark** for either of the following answers, or for both. She loved him. She thought her father would kill her because she helped Theseus.	1
9	2d	**Award 1 mark** each for any **two** of the following: She decided to help Theseus. / She gave Theseus a ball of string to help him. / She asked Theseus to take her back to Athens with him. / She described her father as cruel: *'To think that I am free of my cruel father …'*.	2
10	2d	Answer related either to continuing to pursue Theseus or to getting her revenge. She waited for a boat to pass and sailed to Theseus to beg him to marry her as she was still in love with him. / She took the next boat home to tell her father what had happened. Her father waged war against the Athenians.	1
11	2b	horror	1
12	2d	**Award 2 marks** for a point and explanation from the text. Aegeus felt heartbroken because he had tried to persuade Theseus not to go in the first place/had warned him of the dangers. / Aegeus was heartbroken because he thought his beloved son had been killed/he knew it was a dangerous thing to do. **Award 1 mark** for an undeveloped point. He was devastated/heartbroken.	2
13	2c	**Award 1 mark** for all **four** correct answers: At the centre of the maze was the Minotaur. *2* Theseus is picked up by the Minotaur. *3* King Minos builds a giant maze. *1* (given) Aegeus presumes that Theseus has died. *5* Theseus and Ariadne sail across the calm seas. *4*	1

Things that go bump in the night!

Qu.	Content domain	Answer & marking guidance	Mark
14	2c	Do you think ghosts exist?	1
15	2b	**Award 1 mark** for finding both examples: 1. children 2. adults	1
16	2a	notion	1
17	2b	**Award 1 mark** for *According to tradition, ghosts are invisible but can permit humans to see them.*	1
18	2c 2b	a) haunted. b) **Award 1 mark** for either of the following: A monk haunts the rear terrace. King Edward VII's secretary died there and haunts it.	1 1
19	2a	residences **Do not accept** other words.	1
20	2b	Elizabeth I	1
21	2d/2a	**Award 1 mark** for answers that refer to his desire to leave the room, e.g. He really wanted to/had a desire to leave the room.	1
22	2a	**Award 1 mark** for *apparently*. Also accept *conjecture*. Only accept **one** word.	1
23	2b	John Brown	1
24	2b	**Award 2 marks** for all **five** correct and **1 mark** for **four** out of five correct answers. George III — room beneath the library (given) a monk — rear terrace Henry VIII — cloisters John Brown — corridors Elizabeth I — library	2
25	2d	**Award 3 marks** for a fully developed, text-based explanation for both positive and negative outcomes. Positive outcomes: money, e.g. tourism brings in money which means palaces can be conserved; improvements can be made to the palaces. Access to the real royal artefacts/sources, e.g. people can see what real palaces look like. Negative outcomes: congestion, e.g. car parks and roads get really busy; money, e.g. entrance prices cost a lot; damage to historic sources, e.g. objects are broken, taken; carpets and floors worn; environment, e.g. grounds get ruined; litter is spread. **Award 2 marks** for a fully developed, text-based explanation of either a positive or a negative outcome. **Award 1 mark** for two undeveloped points.	3
26	2f	**Award 1 mark** for all **four** correct answers. Do you believe in ghosts? — introduces the debate about whether or not ghosts exist What is a ghost? — gives information about the description of a ghost Ghosts at royal residences — highlights the different ghosts that lived in palaces and castles Royal ghosts – at what cost? — presents the differing viewpoints on having ghosts	1

The lion and Albert

Qu.	Content domain	Answer & marking guidance	Mark
27	2a	famous	1
28	2b	**Award 1 mark** for correctly finding and copying a line which includes dialect words, e.g. *'E'd a stick with an 'orse's 'ead 'andle.*	1
29	2c	The family were bored by the seaside so they went to the zoo.	1
30	2b	**Award 1 mark** for **two** animals. lions / tigers / camels	1
31	2d	He didn't think it was right that he should be lying so peacefully. / He thought lions were supposed to be ferocious, so he wanted to do something to make him act like this.	1
32	2g	To show that he didn't have much fear. / To show he wasn't one tiny bit scared.	1
33	2b	He poked his stick in the lion's ear.	1
34	2d	**Award 3 marks for two acceptable points, at least one with evidence.** He is brave/fearless because he knew the lion was ferocious and wild but he still approached it. He is naughty/badly behaved because he pushed the stick into the lion's/Wallace's ear even though he was lying peacefully. **Award 2 marks for either two acceptable points, or one acceptable point with evidence.** He is brave/fearless and naughty. **Award 1 mark for one acceptable point.** He is brave.	3
35	2d	**Award 1 mark** for stating that he is wearing his best clothes. Also accept a quote from the text: *All dressed in his best.*	1
36	2d	**Award 2 marks** for one feeling with evidence from the text. Mother is angry/annoyed/cross because the lion had eaten Albert and she had paid to come in. Other reasons: because she had turned a bit awkward and felt that someone had to be summoned / because she says that she is not wasting all of her life to have children and then feed them to the lions. **Award 1 mark** for one acceptable point. Mother is angry/annoyed/cross.	2
37	2d	life is unpredictable.	1
38	2f	to entertain	1
39	2h	Accept a comparison between initial worry/vex from Mother and then the feeling of not too bothered. At first she is *vexed* or worried. Then she says she is not having any more children to feed lions. At the end of the poem, she does not seem too bothered about Albert.	1

Test 2

Lighthouse history

<table>
<tr><th>Qu.</th><th>Content domain</th><th>Answer & marking guidance</th><th>Mark</th></tr>
<tr><td>1</td><td>2b</td><td>Award 2 marks for two correct reasons given in the text.
To mark major headlands and sandbanks. To offer light at entrances to ports, harbours and rivers.</td><td>2</td></tr>
<tr><td>2</td><td>2b</td><td>Award 1 mark for each correct answer. Up to a maximum of 3 marks.
storms / bad weather / avoiding reefs, headlands, sandbanks, cliffs / making safe passage into ports and harbours</td><td>3</td></tr>
<tr><td>3</td><td>2b</td><td>Award 1 mark for answers that suggest that it was to help ships reach their destinations safely.</td><td>1</td></tr>
<tr><td>4</td><td>2b</td><td>Award 1 mark each for any two of the following:
By the 17th century, lights along the east coast helped to guide colliers carrying coal from the ports of the north-east to London.
The coal trade from Newcastle and Sunderland to London dominated coastal traffic.
Just less than 50% of shipping in the period 1779 to 1884 was devoted to coal carriage.
The coal trade was the largest single activity of coastal shipping during the industrial revolution.</td><td>2</td></tr>
<tr><td>5</td><td>2a</td><td>took over/led/ruled/made up the greatest part of</td><td>1</td></tr>
<tr><td>6</td><td>2b</td><td>Award 1 mark for answers that refer to it being the single biggest activity, e.g. it says that it was the largest single activity of coastal shipping during the industrial revolution.</td><td>1</td></tr>
<tr><td>7</td><td>2b</td><td>75 ft</td><td>1</td></tr>
<tr><td>8</td><td>2f</td><td>Award 1 mark for both of the following:
to keep the reader engaged with the text
to provide extra information</td><td>1</td></tr>
<tr><td>9</td><td>2d</td><td>Children may or may not quote. Answers must refer to the link between David's lie to his son and the idea for a book/story where a lighthouse keeper gets his lunch on a wire.</td><td>1</td></tr>
<tr><td>10</td><td>2c</td><td>Award 1 mark for answers related to her name and/or the role of Grace Darling:
The story of Grace Darling / Grace Darling and the shipwreck of Forfarshire / Grace Darling rescues survivors of shipwreck / The role of Grace Darling / Survivors of shipwreck rescued</td><td>1</td></tr>
<tr><td>11</td><td>2b</td><td>Award 1 mark for correctly stating that Grace Darling is famous for helping her father rescue survivors from the shipwrecked Forfarshire.</td><td>1</td></tr>
<tr><td>12</td><td>2b</td><td>Award 2 marks for all four correct answers and 1 mark for two or three correct answers.
The Pharos lighthouse was built. 283 BC
Grace Darling was born. 1815
The Forfarshire was shipwrecked. 1838
Roker Pier lighthouse was built. 1903</td><td>2</td></tr>
<tr><td>13</td><td>2b</td><td>Award 1 mark for two correct answers and 2 marks for all three correct:
<table>
<tr><th></th><th>True</th><th>False</th></tr>
<tr><td>The Pharos lighthouse was 200 metres tall.</td><td></td><td>✔</td></tr>
<tr><td>Almost 100% of coastal shipping in the period 1779 to 1884 was devoted to coal carriage.</td><td></td><td>✔</td></tr>
<tr><td>The lighthouse was tapered for stability.</td><td>✔ (given)</td><td></td></tr>
<tr><td>Grace Darling died aged 26.</td><td>✔</td><td></td></tr>
</table></td><td>2</td></tr>
<tr><td>14</td><td>2f</td><td>to inform</td><td>1</td></tr>
</table>

The hollow land

<table>
<tr><th>Qu.</th><th>Content domain</th><th>Answer & marking guidance</th><th>Mark</th></tr>
<tr><td>15</td><td>2d</td><td>Award up to 2 marks:
1 mark related to the shape created by the miners. 1 mark for references to the absence left by the miners. The miners have gone so all that is left is the hollow, created when they were digging out coal.</td><td>2</td></tr>
<tr><td>16</td><td>2d</td><td>Award 1 mark for any two of the following:
They will mow all day and through the night.
It takes all members of the family to help.
They didn't finish the High Field until tea-time and then they began the Home Field.
By ten or eleven o'clock at night they are still working.</td><td>2</td></tr>
<tr><td>17</td><td>2d</td><td>Award 1 mark for two answers:
They can afford to buy packaged food, so they must be wealthy.
They can afford to keep dogs as pets rather than as working animals.</td><td>1</td></tr>
<tr><td>18</td><td>2g</td><td>It spreads across the hillside.</td><td>1</td></tr>
<tr><td>19</td><td>2a</td><td>racket</td><td>1</td></tr>
<tr><td>20</td><td>2b</td><td>Award 1 mark for three correct or 2 marks for all four correct:
<table><tr><th></th><th>True</th><th>False</th></tr><tr><td>The hollow land used to have miners working there.</td><td>✔</td><td></td></tr><tr><td>There are lots of farming families living in the hollow land.</td><td></td><td>✔</td></tr><tr><td>There are wild horses in Wateryate Bottom.</td><td>✔</td><td></td></tr><tr><td>A big family live in Bell Teesdale's gran and grandad's old house.</td><td>✔</td><td></td></tr></table></td><td>2</td></tr>
<tr><td>21</td><td>2b</td><td>Award 1 mark each for any two of the following:
The racket they make can be heard as far as Garsdale. / They have music playing, lads yelling and laughing and a radio or two going. / Their telephone rings.</td><td>2</td></tr>
<tr><td>22</td><td>2h</td><td>Award 1 mark each for any two of the following:
They are from the city. / They buy, rent or lease the little houses. / They have big estate cars, not a tractor. / They eat packet food. / They're noisy. / The mother cooks Italian-style food. / They have a fridge and a telephone. / The Batemans' dog is a pet whereas the Teesdales' dogs are working dogs. / The Batemans play loud music and listen to the radio.</td><td>2</td></tr>
<tr><td>23</td><td>2b</td><td>Award 1 mark for answers that refer to them being out all night doing the hay/at hay-time.</td><td>1</td></tr>
<tr><td>24</td><td>2g</td><td>Award 1 mark for it's really noisy/loud or a similar description.</td><td>1</td></tr>
<tr><td>25</td><td>2d</td><td>the London family</td><td>1</td></tr>
<tr><td>26</td><td>2e</td><td>Award 2 marks for an explanation related to Mr Bateman being cross with the noise and with reference to the text. For example, Mr Bateman might come out and shout at the Teesdales for making noise because now it is 11 o'clock and they want to go to bed/the tractor is making a racket.
Award 1 mark for a simple explanation with no reference to the text.
He might come out and shout. / He might be cross at the noise.</td><td>2</td></tr>
</table>

The Lady of Shalott

Qu.	Content domain	Answer & marking guidance	Mark
27	2d	**Award 1 mark** for reference to the fact that the countryside is completely covered by fields of barley and rye. / It is completely covered in long fields of barley and of rye.	1
28	2g	It is suitable because the water is chilly so the daffodils are shaking/shivering with the cold. / So you can imagine the daffodils shaking with cold as they stand next to the chilly water.	1
29	2g	The Lady of Shalott's voice is so beautiful that it sounds out of this world/sent from heaven.	1
30	2b	They can hear her chanting and singing.	1
31	2b	**Award 1 mark** for **two** different answers. She lives in a tower. / She wears a pearl garland around her head. / She sleeps on a velvet bed. / She is dressed in royal clothing (*apparelled*).	1
32	2b	She has to weave night and day.	1
33	2b	*To weave the mirror's magic sights*	1
34	2d	**Award 3 marks** for **two** acceptable points (impressions), at least one with evidence. She is bored because she has no time for sport and play. She is unhappy/has little joy because she has to weave all day and has a curse on her. She is unhappy because she says she is *half sick of shadows.* **Award 2 marks** for either **two** acceptable points, or **one** acceptable point with evidence. She is unhappy and bored. **Award 1 mark** for **one** acceptable point. She is unhappy.	3
35	2d	Her weaving/threads.	1
36	2c	**Award 1 mark** for **two** answers: is inside a tower. is under a curse.	1

Test 3

Crystals

Qu.	Content domain	Answer & marking guidance	Mark
1	2b	**Award 2 marks** for all **three** correct answers and **1 mark** for **two** correct answers. perfection/transparency/clarity	2
2	2b	ice	1
3	2c	Where can crystals be found?	1
4	2b	**Award 1 mark** each for any **two** of the following: freezer, fridge, washing machine, TV, telephone, radio, camera, bikes, cars	2
5	2b	**Award 1 mark** for each correct answer. Maximum **2 marks.** Used in control circuits/machines/communications/medicine/diamond blades/scalpels for surgery.	2
6	2h	**Award 1 mark** each for any **two** of the following: They do not corrode; others do. / They are the hardest crystal. / They can be used in surgery. / Other crystals are not used in surgery. **Do not accept** 'Diamonds are colourless'.	2
7	2b	F. Mohs	1

Qu.	Content domain	Answer & marking guidance	Mark
8	2b	**Award 1 mark** for **all four** correctly ordered: diamond *1* (given) topaz *2* apatite *3* fluorite *4* gypsum *5*	1
9	2a	shine	1
10	2b	To cut and polish stones. / To turn stones into objects of beauty.	1
11	2c	**Award 2 marks** for all **five** correct and **1 mark** for **four** out of five correct answers. Did you know? — explains what a material is (given) Crystals at home — highlights how everyday objects are crystalline Fact — gives information about how diamonds do not corrode Hardness — gives information about how hard particular minerals are Making them sparkle! — explains how rough crystals can be transformed	2
12	2d	**Award 2 marks** for all four correct and **1 mark** for **three** correct answers. (see table below)	2

	Fact	Opinion
We live in a crystal planet.	✔	
Water is made from hydrogen and oxygen.	✔	
A crystal's colour can be its most striking feature.		✔
Some crystals are beautifully shaped.		✔

Macavity, the mystery cat

Qu.	Content domain	Answer & marking guidance	Mark
13	2g	**Award 1 mark** for an explanation of the word *master* and **1 mark** for an explanation of the word *criminal*. For example, the word *criminal* suggests that Macavity is breaking the law deliberately and the word *master* suggests that he is very good at it.	2
14	2a	bafflement	1
15	2d	**Award 2 marks** for a developed response that recognises he is clever. For example: Macavity is an intelligent cat so he doesn't leave any evidence of what he's done. **Award 1 mark** for a simple response. For example: He is too clever to be caught.	2
16	2d	That he is very agile and can climb walls/buildings, etc. very easily.	1
17	2b	**Award 1 mark** for each correct answer. Maximum of **2 marks**. His coat is dusty from neglect. / His whiskers are uncombed. / He doesn't wash.	2
18	2b	a snake	1
19	2g	**Award 1 mark** for answers that refer to Macavity as being a monster/evil/villain dressed up like a cat. For example: It suggests that Macavity is evil.	1
20	2b	*'It must have been Macavity!'*	1
21	2b 2d	**Award 1 mark** for each correct answer. Maximum of **2 marks.** He does things that are impossible for a cat to do: breaks the law of gravity/cheats at cards/steals jewels/steals plans/does long division sums.	2
22	2a	clever and thoughtful	1

The travels of Marianne North

Qu.	Content domain	Answer & marking guidance	Mark
23	2b	Because women rarely travelled alone.	1
24	2a	favourite thing/love/passion/hobby/obsession	1
25	2b	She wanted to paint (the intriguing) Monkey Puzzle trees.	1
26	2d	**Award 2 marks** for developed responses with reference to the text. For example: She includes details of many flowers and plants she has seen or painted. The flower names often use scientific words for plants such as Roystonea regia. She knows about science to know all these names. **Award 1 mark** for simple response with reference to the text. She knows the other/real names of many flowers like Roystonea regia. She knows the names of many flowers like Roystonea regia.	2
27	2g	She wrote many long diary entries. / She kept a diary for a long time/many years.	1
28	2b	royal palms	1
29	2g	**Award 1 mark** for answers referring to the rough texture of the flower. For example, it tells you that the flower was rough or prickly which gives you an image of what it looked like.	1
30	2d	**Award 1 mark** for answers that refer to the fact that she used local forms of transport that ordinary people would use. **Award 1 mark** for an example from the text. For example: She used local/normal forms of transport, such as riding on the back of a mule/ travelling in a jampany/riding in a mule-drawn cart/travelling on a steamship/riding on horseback/riding in a train/being carried in a jinricksha and a palki.	2
31	2d	**Award 3 marks** for **two** acceptable points, at least **one** with evidence. She still travelled because she enjoyed travelling and knew that there would be lots of adventures. She wanted to discover different plants because it says that, *my first work was to attempt to make a sketch of the great avenue of royal palms.* **Award 2 marks** for either **two** acceptable points, or **one** acceptable point with evidence. She enjoyed travelling and she wanted to discover different plants. **Award 1 mark** for **one** acceptable point. She enjoyed travelling.	3
32	2c	was a Victorian artist.	1
33	2d	**Award 3 marks** for **two** acceptable points, at least **one** with evidence. Award marks for answers that refer to what she does even though she has to overcome certain hurdles. For example: She was determined because she supported women even though some of them *irritated* her and *made stupid remarks*. She was also determined because even though she was ill, she still travelled to Chile to *paint the intriguing Monkey Puzzle trees.* **Award 2 marks** for either **two** acceptable points, or **one** acceptable point with evidence. For example: She supported women and she painted Monkey Puzzle trees even though she was ill. **Award 1 mark** for **one** acceptable point. She supported women.	3
34	2b	Award **1 mark** for all **four** correct answers.	1

	True	False
Marianne North's mother and father died at the same time.		✔
Marianne reached Lisbon on 13th August at sunrise.		✔
In South Africa Marianne saw stamens dancing.	✔	
Marianne North retired to a house in Gloucestershire.	✔	